Fatigue Effects in Bulk Lead-Zirconate-Titanate

dem Fachbereich Material- und Geowissenschaften
der Technischen Universität Darmstadt

zur Erlangung des akademischen Grades
Doktor - Ingenieur
(Dr.-Ing.)

genehmigte Dissertation von
Dipl.-Ing. Cyril Verdier
aus Clermont-Ferrand, Frankreich

Referent:	Prof. Dr. J. Rödel
Koreferent:	Prof. Dr. H. von Seggern
Tag der Einreichung:	17. Dezember 2003
Tag der mündlichen Prüfung:	19. Februar 2004

Darmstadt 2003
D17

Berichte aus der Materialwissenschaft

Cyril Verdier

Fatigue Effects in Bulk Lead-Zirconate-Titanate

D 17 (Diss. TU Darmstadt)

Shaker Verlag
Aachen 2004

Bibliographic information published by Die Deutsche Bibliothek
Die Deutsche Bibliothek lists this publication in the Deutsche
Nationalbibliografie; detailed bibliographic data is available in
the internet at http://dnb.ddb.de.

Zugl.: Darmstadt, Techn. Univ., Diss., 2004

ISBN 3-8322-2618-4
ISSN 1618-5722

Shaker Verlag GmbH • P.O. BOX 101818 • D-52018 Aachen
Phone: 0049/2407/9596-0 • Telefax: 0049/2407/9596-9
Internet: www.shaker.de • eMail: info@shaker.de

Danksagung, Acknowledgement, Remerciements

Diese Arbeit wurde in der Zeit von Januar 2001 bis Dezember 2003 im Fachgebiet Nichtmetallisch-Anorganische Werkstoffe des Fachbereichs Material- und Geowissenschaften der Technischen Universität Darmstadt durchgeführt.

Herrn Prof. Dr. Jürgen Rödel gilt mein spezieller Dank für die interessante Aufgabenstellung und seine ausgezeichnete Betreuung. Ich habe ihn als jemanden kennengelernt, dessen besonderer Führungsstil und guter Instinkt für richtige Entscheidungen beispielhaft ist, und der mich mit einem offenen Ohr für alle Fragen und Probleme in meiner Arbeit begleitet hat.

Herrn Priv. -Doz. Dr. Doru Lupascu danke ich herzlich für die sowohl fachlichen, als auch freundschaftlichen Gespräche, in denen er mir seine Begeisterung für die Wissenschaft vermittelt hat. Außerdem bin ich ihm für seine übermenschliche Geduld und seine ständige Bereitschaft, meine zahlreichen Fragen zu beantworten besonders dankbar. Eine bessere Betreuung hätte ich mir nicht vorstellen können.

Herrn Prof. Dr. Heinz von Seggern danke ich für die Möglichkeit, Messungen in seiner Arbeitsgruppe durchzuführen und für die ausgezeichnete Zusammenarbeit. Darüber hinaus gilt ihm mein Dank für die konstruktiven Diskussionen und die Übernahme des zweiten Gutachtens.

Dipl. -Ing. Emil Aulbach und Michael Weber möchte ich für ihre ausgezeichnete, präzise und schnelle technische Hilfe danken.

Dennis Braun danke ich für seine sehr gute Probenvorbereitung und Literaturbeschaffung.

Den Mitgliedern der Nichtmetallisch-Anorganische-Werkstoffe Gruppe danke ich für das wirklich hervorragende Arbeitsklima und für ihre freundschaftlichen Verbindungen.

Herrn Dr. Jürgen Nuffer danke ich für seine hervorragenden, vorangegangenen Arbeiten und seine Hilfe bei der Einarbeitung in mein Projekt.

i

I would like to thank Prof. James Scott, Dr. Finlay Morrison, Dr. Matthew Dawber, Dr. Andreas Rüdiger for the very nice and instructive time in Cambridge, and for an excellent scientific cooperation.

Herrn Prof. Dr. Sergei Fedosov und Dipl. -Phys. Jörg Zimmermann danke ich für ihre Hilfe während der Messungen, die ich in der Arbeitsgruppe Elektronische Materialeigenschaften durchgeführt habe.

Dipl.-Ing. Claudia Fasel und Dr. Robert Kolb danke ich für ihre Hilfe bei den Impedanzmessungen.

I would like to address special thank to Nicole Marx for her precious help during the writing up of this work and for her friendship.

Der Deutschen Forschungsgemeinschaft danke ich für die finanzielle Förderung dieser Arbeit.

Enfin, je souhaite remercier de tout coeur mes parents pour leur affection et leur soutien indéfectible. Merci de m'avoir donné toutes les chances possibles de réussir.

Contents

Chapter 1

Introduction

Since the discovery of ferroelectricity in single crystal Rochelle Salt in 1921 and its sub-sequent extension in the realm of polycrystalline ceramics (barium titanate) during the 1940s, there has been a continuous succession of new materials and technological research leading to the development of industrial applications. Ferroelectric materials are nowa-days found in a wide range of applications, from piezoelectric components and optical devices to ferroelectric memories in microelectronics. Among other uses, these include sonic and ultrasonic sensors and actuators, ultrasonic motors, high precision positioning devices, optical switches and ferroelectric random access memories, and many new appli-cations are in the process of being developed. Because these applications have reached the wider consumer market, there has been a call for more stringent requirements in long-term reliability.

The major problems encountered concerning the reliability of ferroelectric materials are the phenomena of ferroelectric fatigue, ferroelectric aging and resistance degradation. Ferroelectric fatigue is the loss of switchable polarization by repeated polarization re-versals. Ferroelectric aging is characterized by a spontaneous change with time in the polarization-voltage response. Resistance degradation is a deterioration of the insulating properties of a dielectric under direct-current bias and elevated temperature.

Although research has been conducted on fatigue for the past thirty years, the phe-nomenon is not well understood and the discussion is still very controversial. It is also complicated by the coupling of electrical to mechanical properties. The mechanical bound-ary conditions, as well as the defect chemistry of the material play a crucial role in this problem.

The material used in this study is a composition of the ternary system lead zirconate-lead titanate (PZT). This is the worldwide most commonly used ferroelectric for several reasons (for example, its low cost, exceptional properties, easy processing and tunability of these properties through doping).

The challenge concerning the fatigue issue is to assign the most fatal degradation of the material, that is, the loss in polarization, to all its microscopic, mesoscopic and macroscopic sources. This work studies the effects of cycling on commercial PZT under unipolar loading and bipolar loading. Unipolar loading is of particular interest because most actuator applications using bulk ceramics are driven this way, whereas bipolar loading is worthy of investigation because it yields a much faster degradation. The material is characterized mostly using electrical measurements. One goal of the project was to understand whether the effects and mechanisms of both loading modes are the same. Furthermore, the fatigue phenomenon was to be investigated in terms of effects of the kinetics of polarization after fatigue and induced changes in the microstructure. With regard to the microstructure, the goal was to introduce a method not yet applied to the fatigue phenomenon in bulk ferroelectrics, impedance spectroscopy. Regarding switching, there have to date been studies in thin films, but no investigations in bulk ceramics.

The majority of data presented in this study was gathered at the Darmstadt University of Technology; part of the results was the product of a collaboration with the University of Cambridge (England).

This work is divided into five sections. First, an introduction about the basics of ferroelectricity and an overview on literature concerning fatigue of ferroelectrics will be presented. Then, the experimental methods and techniques will be described, followed by the experimental results. In the forth section, results will be discussed as well as the correlation between the changes in macroparameters and their microscopic origin. Finally, the possible mechanisms for the fatigue phenomenon will be proposed.

Chapter 2

Theory

This section intends to give an overview of the basics on piezoelectricity and ferroelectricity, present the problem of fatigue and outline the present knowledge on fatigue effects in ferroelectrics. For further details the reader is referred to [1, 2, 3].

2.1 Ferroelectricity and Related Properties

2.1.1 Polarization

A dielectric material is said to be polarized when a limited rearrangement of charges occurs due to the application of an externally applied electric field. There are several ways to obtain this charge displacement: through a small displacement of the electrons in an atom relative to the nucleus (atomic polarization), in ionic materials the relative displacement of cation and anion sublattices (ionic polarization), the orientation of existing dipoles (dipolar polarization) or the transport of space charges to potential barriers such as grain boundaries or phase boundaries (space charge polarization).

The polarization vector is defined as the dipole moment per unit volume and can vary from region to region:

$$\mathbf{n} \cdot \mathbf{P} = \frac{\delta p}{\delta V} = \sigma_p \quad [C/m^2] \tag{2.1}$$

where δp is the dipole moment and $\mathbf{n}$ the outside normal to the external surface. A polarized material can be seen as made up of elementary dipoles, the end faces of which carry surface charge densities of $+\sigma_p$ and $-\sigma_p$ and the polarization of which is equivalent to a surface charge density of bound charges at the sample surface. If we consider the case of a plate capacitor filled with a dielectric, the total surface charge density that is induced in the material by the applied field E is given by the dielectric displacement vector, D:

$$D_i = \varepsilon_0 E_i + P_i [C/m^2] \tag{2.2}$$

where the scalar $\varepsilon_0 = 8.854 \cdot 10^{-12}$ [F.m^{-1}] is called dielectric permittivity of vacuum. If the dielectric is linear:

$$P_i = \varepsilon_0 \chi_{ij} E_j \tag{2.3}$$

$$D_i = \varepsilon_0 E_i + \varepsilon_0 \chi_{ij} E_j = (\delta_{ij} + \chi_{ij}) \varepsilon_0 E_j = \varepsilon_{ij} E_j \tag{2.4}$$

where the χ_{ij} and ε_{ij} are second rank tensors called dielectric susceptibility and dielectric permittivity and δ_{ij} is Kronecker's symbol ($\delta_{ij} = 1$ for i = j, $\delta_{ij} = 0$ for i ≠ j) . If P and E are collinear, χ_{ij} and ε_{ij} are scalars.

2.1.2 Piezoelectricity

Piezoelectricity characterizes the ability of a crystal to develop electric charge on its surface when mechanical stress is exerted onto it. This is the direct piezoelectric effect and is linear. An applied electric field, on the other hand, induces a linearly proportional strain in the material, this is the converse piezoelectric effect.

$$D_i = d_{ijk} T_{jk} \tag{2.5}$$

$$S_{ij} = d'_{kij} E_k \tag{2.6}$$

where T_{jk} (N m^{-2}) is the stress tensor and S_{ij} the strain tensor. d_{ijk} (C N^{-1}) is the third rank tensor of piezoelectric coefficients. Thermodynamic considerations show that $d_{ijk} = d'_{kij}$, that is, the coefficients that connect the field and strain are the same as those that connect the stress and dielectric displacement [4].

Piezoelectric materials convert mechanical energy into electrical energy and vice versa. The electromechanical coupling coefficient, k, is the fraction of the square root of the total mechanical energy converted to electrical energy (or the electrical energy converted to the mechanical energy) over the input mechanical energy (or input electrical energy). Values of k in useful piezoelectrics vary between 0.05 to 0.94.

In ferroelectrics where the strain is non-linear with applied electric field, the piezoelectric coefficient is defined as the change of the strain for moderate change of the electric field:

$$d_{ijk} = \frac{dS_{jk}}{dE_i} \tag{2.7}$$

According to Neumann's principle, symmetry elements of all physical properties of a material must include all symmetry elements of the crystallographic point group of the material. Piezoelectricity can only appear in a non-centrosymmetric structure. Among the 32 point groups, 11 are centrosymmetric and one point group (432) does not allow piezoelectricity. Crystals that belong to the remaining 20 non-centrosymmetric groups can exhibit the piezoelectric effect.

2.1.3 Pyroelectricity

Ten piezoelectric point groups are termed polar because they have a unique polar axis. They exhibit an electric dipole moment even in the absence of an external electric field. The polarization associated with the existence of these spontaneously formed dipoles is called spontaneous polarization. The pyroelectric effect is defined as the change of the spontaneous polarization with temperature in the absence of an external field. The pyroelectric coefficient p_i ($C\ m^{-2}K^{-1}$) is expressed as:

$$\Delta P_i = p_i \cdot \Delta T \tag{2.8}$$

All polar materials are non-centrosymmetric and therefore are also piezoelectric, but not all piezoelectric materials are polar and therefore not all piezoelectrics exhibit pyroelectricity (for example: SiO_2).

2.1.4 Ferroelectricity and Ferroelasticity

Ferroelectric crystals are polar crystals in which the direction of the spontaneous polarization can be switched by applying an external field and the polarization remains at a remanent value (remanent polarization) upon the removal of the electric field. Thus, all ferroelectric materials are pyroelectrics, but only some pyroelectric materials may be switched by an external field and thus be ferroelectrics. This property yields the hysteretic nature of the polarization dependence on the external field analogous to the ferromagnetic hysteresis loop. Similarly, ferroelastic materials exhibit a spontaneous strain which may be reoriented under external mechanical stress.

2.1.5 Electrostriction

Electrostriction is defined as the quadratic relation between an applied electric field and the resulting strain which occurs in all materials. The coefficient of electrostriction M ($N\ m^{-2}\ V^{-2}$) is given by:

$$S_{ij} = M_{ijkl}E_k E_l \tag{2.9}$$

where M_{ijkl} is a fourth-rank tensor. If the dielectric susceptibility is introduced from equation (2.3), the electrostrictive effect can be expressed in terms of polarization:

$$S_{ij} = Q_{ijkl}P_kP_l \qquad (2.10)$$

where Q_{ijkl} is a fourth-rank tensor.

In ferroelectrics, the piezoelectric effect may be interpreted as the electrostriction biased by the spontaneous polarization. Assume we apply a strong DC electric field and a small AC electric field on a ferroelectric material. For simplicity we omit tensor indices. We then have:

$$dP = \epsilon_o \cdot \chi(P(E)) \cdot dE \ , \qquad (2.11)$$

where $\chi(P(E))$ becomes dependent on the polarization. If we differentiate (2.10), we arrive at:

$$dS = 2Q \cdot P(E) \cdot dP \qquad (2.12)$$

and from (2.7)

$$d(P(E)) = 2\varepsilon_0 \cdot \chi(P(E)) \cdot Q \cdot P(E) \qquad (2.13)$$

It can be seen that the piezoelectric coefficient is dependent on the electrostrictive coefficient and the polarization. This is the property exploited in actuators. Whereas the electrostriction is a property of the material, depending on the crystal structure and the bonds between atoms and ions, the piezoelectric coefficient depends on the polarization state, that is on the externally applied field, the boundary condition, the defects in the microstructure, and the history of the material.

2.1.6   Ferroelectric Properties

Phase Transition

Most ferroelectric materials transform into the ferroelectric state from a paraelectric phase at high temperature. The phase transformation temperature is called Curie temperature T_c. The paraelectric phase can be piezoelectric or not and is rarely polar. Upon the phase transition, the material undergoes a change in its structure. It can be shown easily with the example of the perovskite structure of lead titanate, $PbTiO_3$ (Figure 2.1). The perovskite structure, which is cubic in the paraelectric phase, can deform into a slightly tetragonal structure when the crystal is cooled down through the ferroelectric phase transition temperature. The spontaneous polarization lies along the c axis of the tetragonal cell and is usually described in terms of shifts of O^{2-} and Ti^{4+} ions relative to Pb^{2+} forming a spontaneous microscopic dipole. In the paraelectric phase the six directions along the three a axes in the cubic cell are equivalent. Thus the spontaneous polarization P_s may arise along any of these directions with an equal probability at the ferroelectric phase transition.

Using thermodynamic functions, it is possible to describe many important features of ferroelectric crystals without considering the microscopic origin of ferroelectricity. This is the Landau-Devonshire theory [1]. Close to the Curie temperature, the electric Gibb's free energy G_1 can be expressed as a Taylor expansion of the polarization. Using appropriate derivatives of G_1 and considering boundary conditions, it is possible to calculate the temperature dependence of the spontaneous polarization, dielectric permittivity, piezo- and pyroelectric coefficients as the effect of the electric field on these properties close to the phase transition. From the expression of G_1, the function E(P) may be derived as a polynomial function of P. The minima and maxima of this function become instability points in the inverse function P(E). This results in the development of the ferroelectric hysteresis loop.

The microscopic origins of ferroelectricity were assigned to lattice dynamics within the so-called "soft mode theory " [5]. The order parameter of the phase transition, i.e. the polarization may be associated with a lattice vibrational mode which exhibits an instability at the phase transition temperature. The mode softens i.e. its frequency goes to zero, when the temperature is cooled toward the phase transition temperature. It gives rise to a reduction in symmetry i.e. the deformation of the unit cell and the relative shift of the ions of opposite signs and then to the formation of a spontaneous polarization.

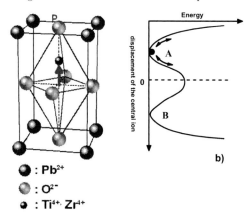

$\bigcirc$: Pb^{2+}

$\bigcirc$: O^{2-}

$\bullet$: $Ti^{4+,}\ Zr^{4+}$

Figure 2.1: a) Perovskite structure which has a tetragonal structure in the ferroelectric phase, b) energy of the central ion relative to its position along the c-axis

Domains

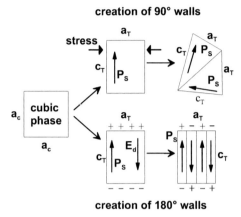

Figure 2.2: Formation of 90° and 180° domains

The directions along which polarization will develop depend on the electrical and mechanical boundary conditions. The interactions between neighboring unit cells result in the formation of regions of uniformly oriented polarization which are called domains. The appearance of spontaneous polarization leads to the formation of surface charges. These produce an electric field called depolarizing field E_d, which is oppositely oriented to P_s. E_d may be very high (in the order of MV·m^{-1}). Its electrostatic energy may be minimized if the created bound surface charges are screened by free electrical charges in the crystal or in the surrounding material (in the electrodes for example), or if the ferroelectric splits into domains with oppositely oriented polarization (Figure 2.2). The wall which separates oppositely oriented domains are called 180° walls. Splitting into domains which have mutually perpendicular polarization orientation may also occur in order to minimize the internal mechanical stresses (Figure 2.2). Their walls are called 90° domain walls. The types of domains which can form depend on the symmetry of the crystal structure. The paraelectric cubic perovskite structure can also deform in a rhombohedral structure at the ferroelectric phase transition. In this case, the polarization develops along the body diagonal (111) of the paraelectric cubic unit cell. This allows for eight possibilities of the spontaneous polarization with 180°, 71° and 109° domain walls. After cooling through T_c without external electric field, ferroelectric grains split into domains of random orientations and the total net polarization is zero (Figure 2.3 a). The material is macroscopically neither pyroelectric nor piezoelectric. The ferroelectric

may be brought into a polar state by applying a high external electric field, this process
is called poling. The domains will reorient in the grains and align as well as possible
along the electric field direction, inducing a net polarization (Figure 2.3 b). The poled
material exhibits pyro- and piezoelectric effects. As the domain orientations are dictated
by the crystallites' orientation and it is not possible to orient the grains, the random
directions of the crystallographic axes of the crystallites limit the extent to which the
spontaneous polarization can develop, and the remanent polarization is always lower than
the spontaneous polarization. Moreover, because of a complex set of internal stresses and
electric fields in grains, not all domains orient into the best position.

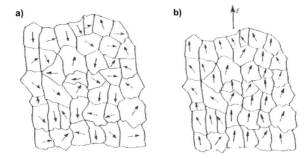

Figure 2.3: A polycrystalline ferroelectric a) before and b) after poling.

Ferroelectric switching and polarization switching

The most important characteristic of ferroelectrics is the polarization and strain hysteresis
loops which can be observed when polarization is reversed by an applied electric field
(Figure 2.4). In the ideal case, the hysteresis can be explained on the scale of the unit
cell. As shown in Figure 2.1 b) the energy of the central ion in terms of its position along
the c-axis takes the form of two wells (Figure 2.1 b). An applied field in the opposite
direction to the polarization shifts the central ion from its energy minimum A toward the
center of the unit cell and the spontaneous polarization is reduced. If the field exceeds a
threshold value, the coercive field E_c, the ion overcomes the energy barrier and jumps into
the other energy minimum B, and the polarization is reversed. When the field is turned
off, the ion stays in B. If the field is reversed and reaches the negative coercive field $-E_c$,
the ion jumps back into the A-position and reverses the polarization once again. This
yields the hysteretic behavior. Corresponding to the change in polarization, a change in
strain occurs when the applied field changes, except that the strain always has a positive

value. Therefore, the strain hysteresis loop can be depicted in a similar manner. On the macroscopic scale, the hysteresis loops are different from the microscopic ones because the domains play a predominant role in the switching process (Figure 2.4). In the unpoled material, the domains have random orientations and the total polarization is zero (point a). If an electric field is applied, the domains with unfavorable direction of polarization switch in the direction of the field, rapidly increasing the total polarization and the strain (point a to b). Once all the domains are aligned, the response becomes linear (point b to c). When the field is removed some domains will ferroelastically switch back, but most of them will stay in the same orientation and the ferroelectric will exhibit a remanent polarization and remanent strain (point c to d). The remanent polarization (and strain) cannot be removed until the electric field in the opposite (negative) direction reaches the coercive field (point e). The domains then switch in the opposite direction within a small increase of field. The polarization and strain will go through a zero point and the polarization will become negative, whereas the strain once again becomes positive. Further increase of the field will cause an alignment of the domains and a saturation of the polarization and strain (point f).

The detailed microscopic mechanism of how the domains reverse is clearly complex and there does not seem to be a universal mechanism valid for polarization reversal in all ferroelectrics. The polarization switching has been considered to occur in several steps: nucleation of new domains, forward growth, sidewise expansion of the domains or finally coalescence [6]. The switching in single crystals or in polycrystals is usually explained by the Kolomogorov-Avrami nucleation and growth model which was later modified for ferroelectrics by Ishibashi and Takagi [7].

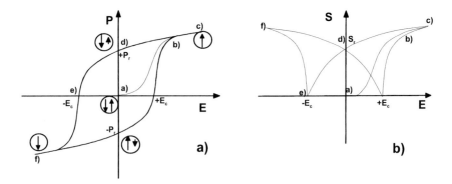

Figure 2.4: a) Polarization hysteresis loop and b) strain hysteresis loop .

2.2 Lead Zirconate Titanate

2.2.1 Phase Diagram

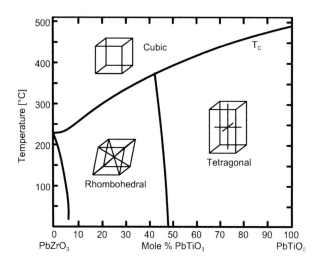

Figure 2.5: Phase diagram of the system $PbZrO_3$ - $PbTiO_3$. The possible orientations of the central ion determining the polar axis are shown in the inserts.

Ferroelectricity does not necessarily originate in crystalline materials. However, due to their very good mechanical properties, single and polycrystalline materials are generally used. Many of these have a perovskite structure (Figure 2.1). The $PbZrO_3$ - $PbTiO_3$ (PZT) system is the most commonly used system in bulk ferroelectric applications. A schematic phase diagram of PZT is shown in Figure 2.5. PZT crystallizes in the perovskite structure with the lead ions on the corners, oxygen ions in face centers and zirconium and titanium in the body center of the unit cell. The structure of the high-temperature paraelectric phase is cubic. Ti-rich (>48 %) composition transforms into a ferroelectric tetragonal structure beneath the Curie Temperature. Zr-rich PZT transforms into an antiferroelectric orthorhombic structure at very low Ti (<5%) content and at room temperature. For Ti content between 5% and 48%, the material is ferroelectric and rhombohedral. From an application point of view, the most interesting compositions lie near the center of the phase diagram where the tetragonal and rhombohedral phases are separated by a boundary which is nearly temperature independent. This boundary is called the morphotropic phase boundary (MPB). The piezoelectric coefficient, electromechanical coupling, dielectric permittivity and remanent polarization reach peak values for a morphotropic composition. At the MPB, the free energy of the tetragonal and rhombo-hedral composition are equal and the material can easily switch between the tetragonal and rhombohedral composition. Thus, the material has effectively more directions along which the polarization may be reoriented by an electric field and the domains can be more easily reoriented.

2.2.2   Doping and Defects in PZT

Ceramics are usually doped in order to modify and tailor their properties for specific applications. A good overview of the effects of doping in PZT is given in [2]. Doping by cations of lower valence (acceptors), either by replacing Pb^{2+} with monovalent cation (e.g. K^+) or by replacing Zr^{4+} or Ti^{4+} with acceptors such as Fe^{3+} or Ni^{2+}, is called hard doping. The substitutions are compensated for by the creation of oxygen vacancies :

$$A_2O_3 + 2MO \rightleftharpoons 2\ M_M + 2A'_{Ti} + 5O_O + V_O^{\bullet\bullet} \tag{2.14}$$

Acceptor ions build defect dipoles with oxygen vacancies. Under an applied electric field, oxygen vacancies can move in the octahedra of the unit cell, and these dipoles can align along the field, even at room temperature. This alignment stabilizes the domain structure and reduces its mobility [8]. This leads to an increase in coercive field, a reduced piezoelectric constants. The dielectric constant and loss are lower, because the domains are less mobile. Moreover, the material has a higher conductivity and exhibits more difficult poling and depoling.

Dopants with higher valence than the substituted ions (donors), e.g. Sb^{5+} in place of Zr^{4+} or Ti^{4+}, or La^{3+} in place of Pb^{2+}, are compensated for by electrons at low oxygen partial pressure and by cation vacancies at high oxygen partial pressure [9].

$$2D_2O_3 + 4TiO_2 \ \rightleftharpoons \ 4D_M^{\bullet} + 4Ti_{Ti} + 12O_O + O_2(g) + 4e' \tag{2.15}$$

$$2D_2O_3 + 3TiO_2 \ \rightleftharpoons \ 4D_M^{\bullet} + 3Ti_{Ti} + 12O_O + V_{Ti}'''' \tag{2.16}$$

Donor-doped PZT, also called soft doped PZT, exhibits high dielectric loss, low conductiv-ity, low coercive field, is easy to pole or to depole and possesses high piezoelectric constant. However, contrary to hard PZT, the properties of soft PZT are not well understood. It is believed that lead vacancies enhance the mobility of domain walls [8].

The most commonly encountered Schottky-defect in PZT stems from the volatility of PbO,

$$O_O + Pb_{Pb} \ \rightleftharpoons \ (PbO)_g + V_O^{\bullet\bullet} + V_{Pb}'' \tag{2.17}$$

yielding PbO vapor in the atmosphere and TiO_2 in the ceramic (in the case of $PbTiO_3$). If either of the two vapor partial pressures P_{O_2} or P_{Pb} is enhanced with respect to the other, the reactions (2.18) and (2.19) furthermore enter the defect balance.

$$O_O \rightleftharpoons \frac{1}{2}(O_2)_g + V_O^{\bullet\bullet} + 2e' \tag{2.18}$$

$$Pb_{Pb} \rightleftharpoons (Pb)_g + V_{Pb}'' + 2h^{\bullet} . \tag{2.19}$$

Neither significant numbers of Ti-vacancies nor interstitials have so far been reported in the literature [10].

At high temperature (above 700 K), the point defects are considered to be in thermal equilibrium and the conductivity is controlled by electronic processes. At room temperature, many of the defects are trapped to a variable degree, the electronic charge carriers are not the most mobile defects and the contribution of ionic conductivity (through vacancies) increases. As the exact nature of the different trapping centers in PZT is not well known, several defect equilibria involving the donor and acceptor ions have to be considered [11].

2.2.3 Processing

Ceramics The manufacturing process of bulk ceramics and thick layers is mainly achieved through the conventional mixed-oxide method. The oxide powders are successively mixed, dried and calcined. The green body is then sintered at temperatures between 1000° C and 1300° C. The external PbO partial pressure is a critical parameter due to the volatility of PbO and its consequences on the properties of the material as mentioned in Section 2.2.2.

An important application of bulk ferroelectric ceramics are multilayer actuators (Figure 2.6). This device is composed of a stack of thin ferroelectric layers (30-80μm) alternated with metal electrodes. This design is advantageous in that only a small voltage is necessary to reach a high strain of the actuator. The structure is assembled before firing and the ensemble is co-fired. Thus the electrodes must have a melting point higher than the sintering temperature. Usually a mixture of palladium and silver is used.

Thin Films The potential applications of thin films as a storage medium has led to the development of several deposition techniques in order to process thin films. In general, there are two major categories of deposition techniques for films: physical vapor deposition, including sputtering and chemical processes, including chemical vapor deposition (CVD) and chemical solution deposition (CSD) (for example sol-gel deposition). An

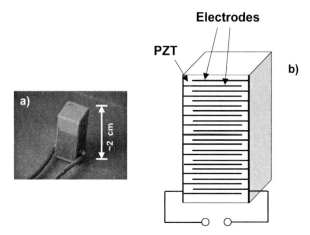

Figure 2.6: a) Photo of a commercial actuator, b) Schematic set-up of a multilayer-actuator

advantage of CSD is the low cost of equipment needed for preparation. In general, the films are processed at high temperatures ($\sim$ 600° -750 °C) in the presence of oxygen. A critical aspect in the fabrication of thin films is the mechanical boundary conditions. Due to the clamping of the films to the substrate, the piezoelectric effect perpendicular to the substrate is reduced. Domain walls seem to be clamped and PZT films behave as hard ferroelectrics [12].

2.3   Fatigue

This chapter intends to give a brief overview of the present knowledge on fatigue in ferroelectrics and especially lead zirconate titanate. There is a large amount of literature on the fatigue phenomenon. Most publications concern fatigue in ferroelectric thin films, fewer deal with fatigue in bulk ceramics. Only few works deal with the effects of unipolar cycling.

The first section of the following discussion will describe the general features of bipolar fatigue after which the different influences of external parameters on fatigue and the microstructural changes induced by bipolar cycling will be outlined. Then the most important models and scenarios on bipolar fatigue will be presented. Finally, present knowledge on unipolar fatigue will be reviewed.

2.3.1   Description of the Phenomenon

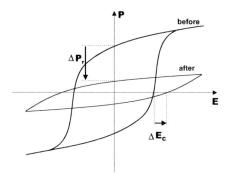

Figure 2.7: Polarization hysteresis loop before and after bipolar fatigue, showing the decrease of polarization and the increase of coercive field

Ferroelectric fatigue is defined as the change of properties of a ferroelectric material under cyclic external loading. In electroceramics, the fatigue usually denotes the effect of electric cyclic loading. In the case of ceramics, the devices are usually cycled unipolar and in some cases also bipolar, whereas thin films are driven bipolar. In this section, we will focus on general changes of the macroparameters induced by bipolar fatigue in the material.

The first work mentioning the influence of alternating fields on a ferroelectric material was given by Merz and Anderson (1955) who studied the fatigue effect in single crystal BaTiO$_3$ [13]. The primary effect of bipolar fatigue is the loss of switchable polarization with increasing cycle number (Figure 2.7). The occurrence of fatigue is usually described by plotting the remanent polarization as a function of the number of switching cycles. An incubation period up to 10^5 cycles is observed followed by a logarithmic loss of polarization and strain up to 10^7 cycles [14, 15, 16, 17] and a saturated stage at higher cycle numbers (Figure 2.8). In some experiments, a small restoration for cycle numbers higher than 10^8 has also been reported, especially in thin films [18, 19].

Accompanying the loss of polarization, a tilt of the polarization hysteresis loop is also observed after fatigue. In thin films, the remnant polarization is usually much smaller than the saturation polarization due to the strong mechanical clamping exerted by the substrate [20]. Thus the hysteresis loop is slanted. During fatigue the slant angle significantly decreases. In contrast, the hysteresis in a bulk material remains fairly squared. The decrease in polarization with respect to cycle number is comparable in thin films and

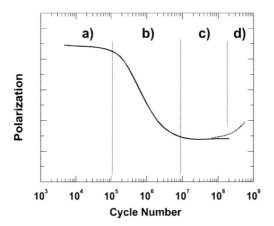

Figure 2.8: Evolution of polarization with the number of bipolar cycles. a) incubation period
b) logarithmic decay c) saturation d) possible restoration

bulk materials. This indicates that some similar mechanisms responsible for fatigue may
occur in both thin films and bulk.

The changes in coercive field are more subtle than the change in polarization. Most
studies report an increase with increasing cycle number [21, 22], but some publications,
especially in thin films, mention a decrease of the coercive field [23, 18]. In bulk PZT,
the change in coercive field starts at slightly lower cycle numbers than the decay in
polarization [17].

The loss of polarization is accompanied by a loss in strain in bulk PZT [24] and thin
films [25]. A corresponding drop of the piezoelectric coefficient d_{33} has been observed [26].
Moreover, in [17, 27] the authors showed in PZT ceramics that parallel to the reduction
of the strain, one of the wings of the strain hysteresis degenerates more rapidly with cycle
number than the other. This asymmetry was also observed in the piezoelectric hysteresis
of PZT thin films [28]. This was attributed to the buildup of fixed internal polarization in
the fatigued material due to the pinning of ferroelectric domains in a preferred orientation
[28, 17] or to the existence of an internal bias field [27].

The dielectric constant at zero field ε_{33} was also found to degrade with cycle number in
bulk PZT [21, 25, 29] as well as in thin films [30], whereas the dielectric constant under high
DC bias was found to be nearly fatigue independent [30, 26]. In [30] the degradation of the
capacitance-voltage curve with cycle number was attributed to a partial suppression of
the domain motion induced by fatigue, also explaining the decay of remanent polarization.

The results concerning the evolution of leakage current with fatigue are contradictory. In fatigued PZT thin films a dramatic increase in leakage current was measured by Scott et al. [31]. It was attributed to a slow release of oxygen from the PZT lattice inducing an accumulation of space charge under the electrodes. Mihara et al. [30] showed that ohmic leakage at intermediate voltage drops with cycle number. They argued that the lead vacancies (as acceptors), present in the sample before fatigue may be compensated by oxygen vacancies (as donors) arising during fatigue, thus leading to a decrease of the leakage current. Stolichnov et al. [32] also found a decrease of the leakage current with fatigue and observed a reduction of the charge to breakdown in fatigued samples. In bulk PLZT, Jiang et al. noticed no significant change in the resistance of the material after fatigue [33].

2.3.2 Characteristics

Electric Field

In bulk PZT, fatigue strongly depends on the amplitude of the cycling voltage. Nuffer et al. [17] showed that fatigue occurred only at fields higher than E_c and increased with increasing field, being strongest when the material is driven far into saturation ($2 E_c$). This indicates that switching is needed to yield fatigue. In [29] the authors also found that higher fields above E_c increase the degradation rate of the polarization and the relative permittivity.

In thin films, fatigue has been found to be virtually independent of the driving field amplitude [18]. However it has also been found to be accelerated for higher amplitudes [34, 16, 35]. Another significant difference from bulk materials is that fatigue is also observed to occur beneath E_c [36].

Temperature

Point defects in the material are known to play a crucial role in fatigue mechanisms. Thus the effect of temperature on fatigue is of interest. A lower fatigue rate with increasing temperatures up to 80 °C has been reported by Kudzin et al. [37] in $BaTiO_3$ and by Duiker et al. [38] in PZT 54/46 thin films. Melnick et al. [39] observed little temperature dependence of the fatigue rate, but the measurements were done in a limited range around room temperature.

On the other hand, several works reported an increasing fatigue rate with increasing temperature in thin film PZT 60/40 (up to 500K) [30, 23] and in PZT 20/80 films (78-423K) [40]. The fatigue rate showed an Arrhenius dependence with temperature giving an activation energy of about 0.05 eV. In [23], the authors ascribe this small activation energy to electron/hole transport and not to ionic defects. But this conclusion did not consider a non-thermal work which cannot be ignored in the case of electric loading.

In bulk PLZT 7/65/35 Jiang et al. [41] showed that fatigue decreased when the temperature increased from 30 °C to 167 °C and that there was no fatigue above T_c. They assigned the fatigue behavior to space charges fixing the domain walls and then hindering switching, and explained the temperature dependence of fatigue through the decrease of maximum polarization at higher temperatures. Wang et al. [29] observed a similar trend in PZT-5H between -20 °C and 100 °C. However, they attributed the degradation to stress-induced cracks and suggested that as the temperature is increased, stresses around internal anomalies are reduced, leading to smaller mechanical failures and thus to less fatigue.

As can be seen from these examples, it appears that the temperature range is crucial in the evolution of the fatigue rate with temperature. The competition between enhanced defect mobility and reduction of the polarization at higher temperature may be relevant.

Frequency

In [42] and [43] the authors reported that the slower the switching, the higher the fatigue rate in PZT thin films. Majumder et al. [44] found in PZT thin films that the loss of polarization due to fatigue was proportional to $\frac{N}{f^2}$; they attributed the origin of this scaling to the drift of oxygen vacancies, the rate limiting process in growth of interface layers at the electrodes responsible for fatigue. Colla et al. [45] observed a reduction in polarization after only 15 cycles by cycling PZT thin films at a very slow frequency (1.7 mHz) with a two steps voltage at E_c and a saturating field. They made a distinction between a domain wall-pinning scenario responsible for fatigue at low frequency and a seed inhibition scenario at higher frequency (see models of fatigue).

Several other publications, however, observed no frequency dependence of the fatigue rate in PZT thin films [18, 35]. In [35] the authors found that in the case of complete switching, fatigue depends solely on the number of switching cycles.

Zhang et al. [46] observed no fatigue in bulk PLZT 2/70/30 when the loading field was applied at high frequencies (5 kHz). However, they did not specify the temperature reached by the sample during cycling. Because of heating during cycling, the Curie temperature may have been exceeded and the sample may have no longer been ferroelectric. Thus, the frequency dependence of fatigue is unclear and may be correlated with the change in temperature.

Crystal and Microstructure

Extensive studies on fatigue in bulk PLZT were performed at Pennsylvania State University [47, 48, 21, 33, 41, 49]. Jiang et al. showed that rhombohedral symmetry (PLZT 7/65/35) exhibits little or no fatigue, whereas tetragonal or orthorhombic compositions (PLZT 8/65/35 and 8.5/65/35) fatigue rapidly [41]. The authors attributed these results to higher mechanical stresses present in the tetragonal and orthorhombic PLZT, which induce microcracking responsible for polarization loss. They also observed that compositions at phase boundaries (ferro/antiferro, ferro/ferro, ferro/para) fatigue most. In [48] they observed in PLZT 7/65/35 that fatigue proceeds faster in samples with higher porosity. They argued that pores act as reservoirs of space charges which are pumped into the grains and grain boundaries during cycling and react with domain walls. The domains are then reoriented into a minimum energy configuration which can no longer be switched by the applied field, thus reducing the polarization. In [33], larger grain size was found to lead to more severe fatigue PLZT 7/68/32. This was attributed to intergranular microcracking caused by stress incompatibilities above a certain grain size. In contrast to the results of Jiang, Lin et al. [50] found no significant degradation in tetragonal PLZT (3/34/66) thin films, whereas rhombohedral PLZT (3/54/46) exhibited severe fatigue.

In PZT thin films, smaller grains were also found to show better fatigue resistance by Yan et al. [51]. The authors explained fatigue mechanisms by the accumulation of defects at the electrode-PZT interface responsible for domain pinning. Thus, the film with a lower fraction of grains touching the electrodes exhibited better fatigue properties.

Lee et al. [52] used a masking technique to produce PZT seeds on a substrate. They found no fatigue in a single grain memory cell, whereas cells with one grain boundary fatigued rapidly. This stresses the important role of grain boundaries in fatigue as a possible defect location and transport path.

In the literature, several modifications of the microstructure or crystal structure have been reported as a consequence of fatigue. An increased degree of texture after fatigue in PZT-5H and PZT-5A was observed by Dausch using X-ray diffraction (XRD) [53]. He interpreted this result through the reorientation of the polar axes from their original directions (parallel to the electric field) as a result of fatigue. In morphotropic PLZT, Pan et al. [54] observed an increased degree of tetragonality at the expense of rhombohedral cells using XRD, and proposed this was due to the gradual build-up of a directional pinning force on the domains, in turn caused by the reorientation of the defects and space charges induced by cycling. Güttler et al. [55] observed the same effect using Raman spectroscopy. Here, the distortion of the lattice was attributed to a loss of oxygen induced by fatigue.

Nuffer et al. [56] carried out a microstructural analysis of morphotropic bulk PZT after fatigue. After chemical etching of the surface of a fatigued sample, they observed etch grooves whose lengths strongly increased with cycle number by scanning electron microscopy. They found increased numbers of these in the middle of the sample as compared to regions near the electrodes. These etch grooves were identified with agglomerates of point defects responsible for domain clamping and polarization loss. The authors also found by TEM that the triple points near the electrodes were weakened after fatigue, indicating a change in their microstructure. This was possibly due to metal migration from the electrodes, silver in this case, into the ceramic via the grain boundaries which acted as high diffusivity paths [57]. Furthermore, they observed a slight shrinkage of the unit cell after fatigue. A possible explanation is that the c/a ratio in the lattice is reduced because of an increased amount of acceptors in fatigued samples, as was shown in [58]. The number of acceptors may have increased because of the recharging of ions during cycling. This was correlated with the change of color of the sample after fatigue. Similar etch patterns were found in PZT thin films by Liu et al. [59] but were identified as microcracks due to strain mismatch at $90°$ domain walls.

Material Modifications

Several material modifications have been developed to improve the fatigue properties of ferroelectrics.

Doping   The effect of doping on fatigue has been dealt with in many articles. In thin films, doping with acceptor species such as Fe [60], Ce [44], Sc [61], Al [62] Na, Mg [63] has been found to positively affect the fatigue resistance. In [60] pairs of stable Fe^{3+}-oxygen vacancies dipoles were interpreted to form, which immobilized oxygen vacancies and hindered their redistribution. In [63] the authors concluded that acceptor dopants postpone the formation of Ti^{3+} defects, resulting in an improvement in endurance. Increased fatigue resistance of Ce doped thin films was explained in [44] by the fact that Ce doping decreases the drift mobility of oxygen vacancies. For soft doping, e.g. for Nb doping, the results in the literature indicate an improvement [64], a deterioration [65] and even an independence [66] of fatigue endurance. Combined donor (Nb, Ta) and acceptor (Sc, Mg, Zn) doping were found to improve the fatigue properties [61]. Chen et al. [67] investigated the effect of doping on the fatigue of bulk $BaTiO_3$ and PZT thin films. They found that donor doping (Nb) significantly improved the fatigue resistance in bulk $BaTiO_3$ compared to acceptor doped (Ca) or undoped materials. A similar but reduced effect was observed in donor-doped PZT thin films. They argued that the addition of donor dopants results in the consumption of oxygen vacancies (see Section 2.2.2). They concluded that the detrimental effect of acceptor dopants and beneficial effect of donor dopants supports the important role of oxygen vacancies in fatigue. In contrast, Jiang et al. [48] and Viehland et al. [68] observed a higher fatigue rate in soft PZT ceramics compared to hard doped PZT. Thus, the effect of doping on electric fatigue of PZT is still controversial and the different processing methods and electrodes used in the reported studies play a significant role in the disparity of the results.

Excess and Deficient Lead Oxide   The role of lead stoichiometry and especially lead vacancies in fatigue is not yet clear. An excess of Pb of 10 % was shown to improve resistance of fatigue in PZT(40/60) thin films by Yang et al. [69], indicating that lead vacancies may play a role in fatigue. However, a 20% excess of Pb in PZT(48/52) thin films resulted in the formation of a secondary PbO_2 phase and degraded fatigue properties [70]. This secondary phase may act as a pinning center for the domains and absorb some oxygen ions during annealing, thus leading to an increase of oxygen vacancies. Moreover, it was shown in [71] and in [72] that the compensation of Pb loss through a $PbTiO_3$ or PbO buffer layer does not improve the fatigue performance of PZT thin films. The authors concluded that Pb stoichiometry does not play a significant role in fatigue. A theoretical work by Pöykkö and Chadi [73] about the stability of the lead-vacancy-oxygen-vacancy pairs also supported the hypothesis that the influence of lead deficiency on fatigue is minimal.

Effect of Hydrogen   In the processing of electronic chips, hydrogen is used as a reducing agent used in the metallization to protect electrodes from oxidation. Kanaya et al. [74] showed that this treatment yields an imprint in the polarization hysteresis of PZT thin films. They observed a segregation of hydrogen underneath the electrodes and attributed the imprint to the formation of oxygen vacancies underneath the electrodes. Thus, hydrogen may have detrimental effects on fatigue properties.

Second Phase or Layer   Besides doping of the material, fatigue properties of ferroelectrics can be improved through the addition of a secondary phase or secondary layer. Zhang et al. showed that the fatigue resistance of bulk PLZT could be improved by the incorporation of SBN ($SrBi_2Nb_2O_9$) [75], SBT ($SrBi_2Ta_2O_9$) [76] or ZrO_2 [77]. The improvement of fatigue resistance was attributed to the fact that oxygen vacancies can easily move in the second phase, avoiding pile-up at domain walls. In PZT thin films, an antiferroelectric additional layer of $PbZrO_3$ [78] reduces the initial remanent polarization but improves the fatigue resistance. In [79], the authors showed that PLZT capacitors with a PZT buffer layer between the ferroelectric and the Pt electrode exhibit fatigue-free behavior. Bao et al. [80] showed that the sandwich structure Pt/BLT/PZT/BLT/Pt (BLT: $(Bi,La)_4Ti_3O_{12}$) exhibits fatigue free behavior. Kim and Basit [81] developed a ferroelectric field-effect transistor incorporating a very thin MgO layer between the ferroelectric and the Si substrate. The fabricated device showed excellent fatigue resistance.

Domain Structure

Changes in the domain configuration have been observed after fatigue. Kudzin et al. [37] showed that the domain structure in single crystal $BaTiO_3$ after fatigue constitutes a configuration of opposing domains with "head-to-head" or "tail-to-tail" arrangements of the spontaneous polarization indicating that some domain walls are charged. Direct observations with AFM of fully clamped polarization regions in thin films [82, 83] confirmed the hypothesis that polarization loss results from the pinning of domain walls.

Lupascu and Rabe [84] observed with AFM in bulk PZT that the domain structure changed from a mostly watermark pattern of rounded contours with $180°$ domain walls before fatigue to a herringbone pattern of needle domains after fatigue. They observed a head-to-head or tail-to-tail configuration around structures which were identified as defect agglomerates responsible for the clamping of domains. SEM observations in the same material [11] showed a change of domain structure after fatigue, indicating an eventual change of structure of the rhombohedral grains into a tetragonal structure. A further set of TEM observations of domains in $BaTiO_3$ and $KNbO_3$ was made by Krishnan et al. [85]. They observed that angled and curved domain walls were abundant and switched very fast because they were charged. They argued that fatigue may arise from domain interlocking that increases the density of charge-compensated domain walls. These domains find a stable energy configuration and cease to switch. Such an interlocking of domain boundaries was observed by Chou et al. [86] in fatigued $(Pb_{1-x}Sr_x)TiO_3$. The domain boundary density increased during polarization reversal. Interactions between the domains led to the formation of zigzag shaped boundaries, domain boundaries became constrained and the polarization switching became more difficult.

Oxygen Partial Pressure and Oxygen Vacancies

There is a fairly large body of evidence in the literature that oxygen vacancies may play an important role in fatigue of ferroelectrics. Oxygen vacancies are known to be the most mobile defects in perovskite oxides at room temperature [87]. By observing the Auger electron spectroscopy depth profiles in fatigued PZT thin films, Scott et al. [31]

and later Mihara et al. [30] found oxygen deficient regions at the interfaces of both electrodes, implying a region of greater oxygen vacancies. Bernstein et al. [88] and especially Brazier et al. [89] showed in PZT thin films that fatigue was strongly dependent on the ambient oxygen partial pressure. Pan et al. [90] observed an oxygen emission from PZT ceramics during cycling. They attributed this to a reduction of the material due to electron injection, inducing the formation of oxygen vacancies. The use of oxide electrodes has been found to significantly improve the fatigue resistance of thin films (see electrodes). This can be attributed to the fact that oxide electrodes act as a sink for oxygen vacancies. Reducing treatment, for example with hydrogen (see effect of hydrogen) during processing degrades fatigue resistance in ferroelectric thin films [74], probably due to the formation of oxygen vacancies at the ferroelectric/electrode interface. In the same manner, reincorporation of O_2 after reduction has been shown to improve fatigue resistance [91]. Wu et al. [92] showed that the processing of PZT thin films with Pt electrodes under low oxygen partial pressure lead to strong fatigue.

In contrast to the results of Pan, Nuffer et al. [93] observed no relevant oxygen liberation from PZT during cycling. Although they assumed a constant concentration of oxygen vacancies during fatigue, they showed that these redistribute during cycling, leading to agglomeration. An tracer study by Schloss et al. [94], using O^{18} as a tracer, showed that there was no long range diffusion of O^{18} during fatigue in PZT thin films. The authors assumed that the observed O^{18} redistribution indicated oxygen vacancy motion, and concluded that oxygen vacancies play a minor role in fatigue. This assumption is however doubtful as, in the densely packed perovskite structure, the probability for an oxygen vacancy to diffuse to a neighboring location is much higher than the probability of an O^{18}.

Point Defects

Besides oxygen vacancies, other point defects have been shown to be involved in the fatigue process. However, their effect on fatigue through interaction with domain walls is not yet well understood.

Extensive studies on point defects and fatigue were performed by the group from Sandia National Laboratories. Warren et al. demonstrated that electronic charge trapping plays a crucial role in fatigue. They showed that a loss of switchable polarization could be induced in PZT thin films [95] and bulk ceramics [96, 95] by illuminating them with band-gap light, which excites electron-hole pairs, while applying a DC voltage just below the coercive field. These data were then correlated with fatigue data. In $BaTiO_3$ crystals, Warren et al. [22, 97] showed that fatigue induces changes in the oxidation states of paramagnetic impurity related centers such as Fe^{3+} or Pt^{3+} through trapping of electronic charge carriers using Electron Paramagnetic Resonance (EPR). They also observed a change in the Fe^{3+}-$V_O^{\bullet\bullet}$ signal during fatigue which was attributed to a deformation of the oxygen octahedron due to the presence of oxygen vacancies. In [97], it was demonstrated in polycrystalline $BaTiO_3$ that alignment of defect dipoles does not occur during fatigue. They also determined Pb^{3+} and Ti^{3+} to exist in PZT [98]. Lenjer et al. [99] proved the existence of Ti^{3+} polarons bound to oxygen vacancies in $BaTiO_3$. Due to interactions with the lattice, they may play a role in fatigue as was suggested by Scott et al. [100]. By cycling PZT thin films under illumination, Lee et al. [101] and Al Shareef et al. [102] also stressed the importance of trapped electronic charge carriers as pinning centers for domain walls . The stronger the illumination, the less the polarization dropped during cycling. This behavior may be due to the recombination of photogenerated carriers with charge injected from the electrode leading to a reduced density of electronic charge carriers. Similarly , Peterson et al. [103] observed a recovery of the polarization in PZT thin films after fatigue by illuminating the fatigued sample. They argued that the created electronic charge carriers re-charge the oxygen vacancies which loose, at least partially, their binding charge to pin the neighboring domains. In bulk PZT, Nuffer et al. [56] observed a change in the color of the sample indicating also a probable change in oxidation states of some ions.

Anisotropy

As mentioned above, fatigue can induce a texture in the material (see crystal and microstructure). Thus it is expected that fatigue effects are more pronounced in some directions than others with respect to the cycling field direction and crystal structure. Pan et al. [54] first showed that the polarization hysteresis loop was unaltered perpendicular to the cycling direction. However, cycling in the perpendicular direction yielded earlier fatigue. The results at an intermediate angle between the cycling and the perpendicular direction gave an average of both directions. They interpreted that cycling aligns oxygen vacancies in a preferred orientation in the unit cell. These create a potential well which hindered the switching of the central cation in one direction. However, the switching is not hindered in the perpendicular direction.

Fatigue effects were also found to be anisotropic with respect to the crystal orientation. Mansour and West [104] investigated the dependence of fatigue behavior of rhombohedral 53/47 PZT thin films on grain orientation. They found that films oriented in the [111]-direction demonstrated better fatigue resistance. The same trend was noticed in [105]. In rhombohedral single crystal PZN-PT ($Pb(Zn_{0.33}Nb_{0.66})O_3$-$PbTiO_3$), Takemura et al.

[106] observed a much better fatigue resistance in the $[001]_C$ direction (the subscript c indicates orientations given in terms of the prototype cubic perovskite axes) compared to the $[111]_C$ direction. For intermediate angles between these two directions they found intermediate damages. They attributed this result to the higher domain mobility of the $[001]_C$ direction. Chu and Fox [107] obtained similar results in PLZT thin films. An interesting point in the observations of Nuffer et al. [56] mentioned earlier (see crystal and microstructure) is that etch grooves were highly anisotropic and assigned to planar defect arrangements parallel to the electrodes.

Electrodes

The influence of electrodes was found to be crucial in the fatigue behavior of thin films, but less in bulk ferroelectrics. The use of metal electrodes has two possible consequences. First, the contact between the electrodes and the semiconductor ferroelectric build a Schottky barrier which induces a space charge layer beneath the metal electrodes. Second, ionic species can hardly diffuse in the metal and may migrate under applied electric fields and accumulate underneath the electrodes. It is difficult to differentiate between these two types of space charge layers, but they have a relevant influence on the fatigue behavior of ferroelectrics.

Brennan [108] proposed a defect chemistry model to explain the formation of a space charge layer close to the electrodes in response to applied fields. He considered the effects of naturally occurring acceptor impurities and oxygen vacancies and their migration to the ferroelectric-electrode interface. Stolichnov et al. [109] showed that conduction in fatigued samples occurred through tunneling mechanisms in PZT thin films with Pt electrodes. They argued that the increase of tunneling conduction could be explained by the presence of a charged interface layer at the electrodes and concluded that this was coherent with a seed inhibition model of fatigue (see Section 2.3.3). However, the partial recovery of the polarization after thermal annealing suggested that a second mechanism played a role in fatigue.

The electrode-ferroelectric interface quality was shown to have a strong influence on fatigue resistance. In bulk PLZT, Jiang et al. showed that the adherence of the electrode to the ceramic was a key factor [110] and that fatigue resistance was very sensitive to surface contaminations [21]. Pan et al. [111] observed in antiferroelectric PLZT that polishing the material surface could improve fatigue resistance. In thin films, the PZT-electrode interface was shown to be improved by a thermal annealing treatment in order to yield enhanced fatigue resistance [112].

The use of oxide electrodes was found to enhance fatigue resistance considerably in many investigations; for example, RuO_x [113], $La_{0.5}Sr_{0.5}CoO_3$ (LSCO) [114], $YBa_2Cu_3O_7$ [115], IrO_x [116] , $BaRuO_3$ [117] were used. The common explanation is that oxide electrodes allow oxygen vacancy diffusion, preventing them to accumulate at the ferroelectric-electrode interface, which is the case for metal electrodes [118]. Following his nearby-electrode injection model (see Section 2.3.3), Tagantsev et al. [119] argued that the oxide electrodes could create a high conductivity network of grain boundaries doped with the component of the oxide, promoting the nearby electrode charge relaxation and thus reducing the fatigue effect. However, Dimos et al. [120] showed that PZT thin films with LSCO electrodes, fatigue free under normal conditions, could be made to exhibit significant polarization fatigue when illuminated by a broad band UV light. They concluded that electronic charge carriers acted as pinning centers for domain walls.

Du and Chen [121] studied the effect of a semi-conducting top electrode in PZT thin films while maintaining a Pt ground electrode. They found that fatigue was strongly reduced for a p-doped Si electrode and slightly for a n-type electrode. They suggested that a p-type electrode reduced the number of free electrons due to a different Schottky barrier height. Electron injection was believed to reduce $V_O^{\bullet\bullet}$ to $V_O^{\bullet}$ which were much more mobile and thus could segregate easier, leading to increased fatigue.

In bulk PZT, Pan et al. [54] and Jiang et al. [21] found that the removal of the original fatiguing electrodes and re-electroding yielded no improvement in the polarization. The authors concluded that the ferroelectric-electrode interface plays only a secondary role in fatigue of bulk PZT. In contrast, Carman et al. [122] found that the polarization of a fatigued PZT sample recovered 90% of its initial value after polishing the fatiguing electrodes and re-electroding the sample, indicating that the interface may be also significant in fatigue of bulk ferroelectrics.

Mechanical Damage

As was demonstrated by Cao and Evans [123], domain switching may initiate microcracks near internal anomalies and cause them to grow and propagate. Various publications have reported the presence of microcracks in bulk material after fatigue in rhombohedral [124] and tetragonal [125] crystal structures. A large portion of local stresses leading to microcracking may be due to electromechanical interactions between domain walls and grain boundaries or heterogeneities originating from defects. Alternatively, microcracks may originate from purely mechanical incompatibilities at electrode edges and other geometrical constraints due to the design of the sample. Rough electrodes can induce field singularities which can lead to strain mismatch between neighboring grains and induce microcracks [110]. Microcracks were observed at the electrodes and in the bulk of fatigued

PZT [56]. Wang et al. [29] noticed microcracks to emanate from voids in the bulk of the material. Further, macroscopic delamination cracks were found near the electrodes as well as macroscopic cracks originating from electrode edges [126]. Weitzing et al. [27] observed that the growth rate of cracks in bulk PZT diminishes with increasing cycle number. They correlated this decrease with the reduction of the strain, which acts as the driving force and becomes too small for further crack extension. Microcracks were shown to reduce the amount of switchable macroscopic polarization [127]. However, it is still unclear wether microcracking is a cause of fatigue and induces the loss of polarization or is a consequence of fatigue.

Rejuvenation

Polarization suppression due to fatigue was shown to be, at least partially, a reversible process. It has been shown that rejuvenation of fatigued PZT thin films can be achieved by applying a high DC electric field after fatigue [18] or a DC field at fatigue voltage for an extended period of time [42]. Warren et al. [128, 129] could restore the polarization of PZT thin films after fatigue only by combining a DC bias voltage with UV light illumination or high temperature. This supports the idea that electronic charge carriers are involved in fatigue. However, further cycling in rejuvenated samples was reported to fatigue the film faster. In bulk PZT, Nuffer et al. [130] showed that the application of a high AC electric field made it possible to remove the asymmetry of the strain hysteresis loop (see Section 2.3.1), but no recovery of the polarization was observed. Recovery of the polarization and strain could be achieved by annealing the fatigued material at temperatures higher than T_c [131, 48, 130, 22]. This was attributed to the fact that both pinned and switchable domains disappeared due to the elimination of spontaneous polarization during heating. When the temperature cooled down through T_c, the domains were formed again without pinning [48]. The fairly high thermal stability of defects responsible for the domain clamping indicates that these may be of ionic nature, e.g. oxygen vacancies [22, 130]. However, a complete recovery was rarely observed. The non-recoverable part was imputed to microcracks [130, 124] or irreversible surface deterioration [48].

Acoustic Emission

Measurements of acoustic emission (AE) were achieved in correlation with fatigue in bulk ferroelectrics in order to detect abrupt local stress or strain changes within the material. Extensive AE were observed in fatigued PLZT with large grain size (18μm) by Jiang et al. [33]. The authors attributed these AE, occurring randomly during a two day cycling experiment at 50Hz, to the macroscopic cracking induced by fatigue near the edges of the electrodes. Nuffer et al.[17] also measured an increasing number of acoustic events after fatigue in morphotropic bulk PZT. During monitoring of polarization hysteresis loops in fatigued samples, they observed higher AE values and lower threshold values for the onset of AE events. They attributed these mostly to the clamping of domain walls induced by fatigue.

Kinetics

The switching of ferroelectrics has been subject of interest in many publications [6]. However, only few report the change of the switching kinetics with fatigue. Scott et al. [132] found in fatigued KNO_3 thin films that the switching time decreased with fatigue. They interpreted that fatigue pinned the slowest switching domains and that the fastest domains remained free to switch, thus leading to a faster switching as the polarization decreased. There are very few experiments of fast switching in bulk ceramics. Levstik et al. [133] found that the switching transient current in bulk PLZT ceramics can be described well with the Avrami model (see Section 2.1.6) but did not measure the change of this transient after fatigue. The model of fatigue by Shur (see Section 2.3.3) based on the Avrami-theory was shown to yield a good fit of polarization hysteresis loops acquired after fatigue in bulk PZT [134] but these hysteresis loops were measured with a triangular pulse at low frequency and did not show the fast switching behavior.

2.3.3   Models of Fatigue

This section intends to give a brief summary of the most important scenarios on fatigue in ferroelectrics which have been presented to date. Several mechanisms have been explained to be at the origin of the reduction in polarization switching after fatigue such as domain wall pinning by point defects, agglomerates of point defects or defect dipoles, inhibition of the seeds before they can create macroscopic domains, changes on the scale of the unit cell, mechanical failures, or growth of conductive dendritic paths. Moreover, some researchers have developed mathematical models to simulate the degradations induced by fatigue.

Domain Wall Pinning

Point Defects   Warren et al. [97] proposed a fatigue scenario based on domain locking due to the trapping of injected and/or created electronic charges at domain boundaries. The charge injection occurs at peak voltage and the trapping occurs near the switching

threshold. The trapped charges are further stabilized by the deformation of oxygen oc-
tahedrons due to the presence of oxygen vacancies. Thus, oxygen vacancies can migrate
and stabilize domain walls at their respective position, the domains become pinned. An
alignment of defect dipoles was not observed. The authors also stress that in addition
to charge injection, charge detrapping can occur at high fields and there is a competition between pinning and unpinning. A fatigue-free behavior occurs when the pinning
rate does not exceed the unpinning rate. The authors measured that alignment of polar
defect-dipoles did not occur during fatigue, showing that they cannot be made responsible
for polarization reduction.

Tajiri and Nozawa [135] developed a quantitative model for ferroelectric thin films
based on the emission of free electrons from trap states in the material. The free electrons,
which are emitted from the traps whenever the polarity of the applied voltage switches, are
captured in domains and pin them. A pair of pinned domains with opposite direction is
neutralized electrically (compensation process). The emission process is assumed to occur
through thermionic field emission and impact ionization. The authors assume the decrease
in polarization to be proportional to the cumulative number of emitted electrons. With
this model, by introducing the energy distribution of trapped levels on thermionic field
emission and the impact ionization rate, the effects of applied voltage and temperature are
successfully simulated. The model also explains the high fatigue resistance in $SrBi_2Ta_2O_9$.

Defect Dipoles   Dawber and Scott [136] presented a fatigue model for bulk $BaTiO_3$
based on the ageing model of Arlt [137, 138, 139]. Under AC cycling, due to migration of
oxygen vacancies in the unit cell, the defect dipoles formed by an oxygen vacancy and the
central ion reorient in the plane perpendicular to the polarization direction. This leads
to pinning of domain walls. The sites of oxygen vacancies n_i $_{(i=1..3)}$ in the unit cell are
modelled by a three potential well system. The hopping of oxygen vacancies from one
site to another is modelled with a 6x6 matrix:

$$\frac{dn_i}{dt} = -a_{ij}n_j \tag{2.20}$$

$$with \ \ a_{ij} = a_0 \exp(\frac{-W_{ij}}{k_bT}) \tag{2.21}$$

where a_0 is the attempt frequency and W_{ij} the activation energy of hopping. Integrating over time and substituting t=N/f yields the expression of change in concentration of
vacancies on sites n_2 perpendicular to P. The authors assume that the switchable polarization is inversely proportional to the concentration of vacancies on sites n_2 which yields
an exponential expression for P(N) (N: cycle number). The second assumption is that
the oxygen vacancy concentration is low in bulk $BaTiO_3$, yielding a higher enthalpy of

annihilation of oxygen vacancies [140]. This accounts for increased fatigue with increasing
temperature in the expression of P(N)(in contrast to thin films fatigue).

Pöykkö and Chadi [141] proposed a microscopic model based on dipolar defects formed
by the combination of oxygen vacancies and impurity metal ions. Their atomic relaxation
calculations showed that a Pt impurity and an oxygen vacancy form a strongly polar complex, which is stabilized by electron capture, and pin the polarization of the surrounding
lattice. In another work [73], they found that lead vacancies and oxygen vacancies do not
have a strong binding. Thus lead vacancies were concluded to play no important role in
fatigue. In a similar way, Lee et al. [52] explained the fatigue mechanism by the rotational
motion of defect dipoles leading to pinning of the domains.

Agglomerates   Brennan [14] modeled the fatigue to be due to the formation of mesoscopic planar structures of charged point defects and opposing domains building self-
stabilizing structures. The incorporation of a charged point defect leads to a reorientation
of the domains in head-to-head or tail-to-tail configurations. Because the domain wall
extends beyond the defect, building opposite charges around it, an additional defect of the
same kind is attracted to the already existing one. The energy is further reduced if the
defect is aligned with its neighbor perpendicular to the polarization. However, interaction between the charged defects results in an activation energy for attaching new defects,
which in turn increases with number of defects already present. This activation energy
is assumed to be proportional to the size of the agglomerate. The second assumption is
that the polarization decay is proportional to the number of defects in these structures.
This leads to the logarithmic decay of the polarization with cycle number. Vacancies
are considered to be the most relevant defects. No crystallographic orientation and no
specific location of the defect agglomerates are specified in this model. The Landau-
Devonshire theory yields the hysteresis form which is biased by the frozen polarization
pinned by the agglomerates. This model predicts a decrease of P_r but also a decrease
of E_c, which opposes common observations in bulk ferroelectrics. This model does not
include considerations of $90°$ domain walls.

Agglomerates under the Electrodes   Yoo and Desu [15, 34, 142] first proposed a
quantitative model which considered the motion of point defects during cycling. This
was designed for thin films. According to their model, a one-directional movement of
defects due to asymmetric polarization and internal field occurs under alternating pulses.
The defects (mainly vacancies) are trapped at electrode-ferroelectric interfaces and/or at
grain and domain boundaries and cause structural damages, which results in polarization
loss. In contrast to the model by Brennan, Yoo and Desu only consider an accumulation

of trapped defects at interfaces rather than the agglomeration in organized structures. They use a standard Ohm's law to express the defect flux density. Ion jumps are activated by the difference of internal field ΔE_i between forward and reversed voltage. They assume that this difference originates from the structural instability and asymmetry of grain boundaries and electrode interfaces. Their second assumption is that the internal field difference will decrease proportional to the number of vacancies which arrive at the interface at a certain time Δj (ionic flux), which is proportional to ΔE_i. It follows that:

$$\frac{d(\Delta E_i)}{dX} = -\zeta \Delta E_i \qquad (2.22)$$

where X is the number of defects trapped at the interfaces. The third assumption is that the change of polarization with respect to trapped defects is proportional to the polarization itself. This yields a power-law expression of P(N)

$$P(N) = P_0(A.N + 1)^{-m} \qquad (2.23)$$

where A is the piling constant and m is the decay constant.

Dawber and Scott [143, 144] proposed a model for fatigue in thin films based on electromigration and agglomeration of oxygen vacancies to the region where the metal electrode joins with the ferroelectric. The oxygen vacancies order preferentially in two-dimensional arrays perpendicular to the polarization direction. They form superlattice structures at 7 % vacancy concentration [140]. This accumulation leads to pinning of domain walls in accordance with the model by Brennan. Like Yoo and Desu, they also use Ohm's law to calculate the flux density of vacancies. Oxygen vacancies, modelled as spherical cavities, experience a modified electric field. Their calculation is based on a single depletion region at the reverse bias junction which implies that the local electric field is much smaller under forward bias than reverse bias. This leads to an ionic current density difference. The influx of charged ions is multiplied by cross section over volume and integrated over time to obtain the change of the concentration of oxygen vacancies with cycle number. The authors assume that the switchable polarization is inversely proportional to the concentration of vacancies near the interface. This yields the exponential expression for P(N). The model is in agreement with experimental data for different frequencies, different voltages and different temperatures. It accounts for faster fatigue at higher temperatures. The model predicts a strong anisotropy of fatigue because the planes of oxygen vacancies occur in fairly specific crystallographic orientation perpendicular to the polar axis.

Du and Chen [121] mentioned that electron injection from the electrode could facilitate fatigue by de-ionization of oxygen vacancies from $V_O^{\bullet\bullet}$ to $V_O^{\bullet}$. $V_O^{\bullet}$ is expected to have a smaller activation barrier for hopping and should segregate more readily.

Agglomerates in the Bulk   Lupascu [11] developed a model based on pinning of domains in the bulk through planar agglomerates of oxygen vacancies. As in Scott's model, the agglomerates are part of {001} planes. The externally applied field is considered insufficient to explain the ionic flux leading to agglomeration. The driving force for defect migration is the local depolarizing field, which is unscreened during small fractions of time during a bipolar cycle just before the domain system switches. This leads oxygen vacancies or other ionic defects to drift and be irreversibly captured in the vicinity of existing agglomerates, as predicted by Brennan. The calculations consider that all ions entering a cylindrical volume beneath one agglomerate are captured into the agglomerate plane. The fatigue saturates when all the isolated defect ions/vacancies have been incorporated into the agglomerates. The model yields an increasing fatigue with increasing temperature according to [23], with decreasing frequency, increasing voltage amplitude and decreasing grain size.

Passive Layer

In thin films, fatigue has been explained by the appearance and growth of a non-ferroelectric layer called passive layer (or dead layer) at the electrode-ferroelectric interface [145, 146, 147]. Several models describing the effects of this layer on the macroscopic properties of the film have been developed. Larsen et al.[145] explained fatigue by the voltage drop through the non-ferroelectric layer, leading to a smaller field seen by the bulk, which becomes insufficient to switch the domains. Bratkovsky and Levanyuk [146], showed that the growth of the passive layer can explain the tilt of the polarization hysteresis loop during fatigue and concluded that this may be the main cause of fatigue.

Seed Inhibition

Tagantsev [119, 45] suggested a different explanation for the polarization loss in thin films after fatigue. Although he supports the predominant role of domain wall pinning at very low frequencies, he explains the polarization loss at driving frequencies, i.e above the kHz, by a seed inhibition mechanism. The switching process can be divided into two stages: nucleation of new domains from the electrodes and growth of existing domains. In this model, the reduction of P is considered to be due to the suppression of the switching ability of the seeds before they can create a macroscopic domain. The seeds are blocked by ionic or electronic defects located near the interface. The scenario is based on nearby electrode injection: electrons and holes are injected from the electrodes into the ferroelectric film, trapped at deep levels and immobilized, producing a simple charge defect leading to seed inhibition. There are several possible origins of the nearby-electrode injection. When a nucleus of inverse polarization appears at the electrode, the bound charges on the interface between it and the rest of the domain produce a high electrical field which can promote charge injection. Alternatively, the existence of a passive layer [148] with a low dielectric constant between the ferroelectric and the electrode can explain the presence of an electric field high enough to induce charge injection. However, Tagantsev stresses that the existence of a growing passive layer is not sufficient to explain the changes of all the macroparameters, specifically the coercive field, after fatigue [149]. This model accounts for the dependence of fatigue on cycle number, frequency (insensitive), amplitude of the applied field, and the loading mode (unipolar or bipolar).

Bonds, Unit Cell

Several authors have attempted to explain fatigue on the scale of a unit cell. Miura and Tanaka [150] developed a fatigue scenario based on calculations of the electronic states of perovskite oxides $ATiO_3$. They relate the magnitude of ferroelectricity to the magnitude of the π bond between Ti^{3d} and O^{2p}. The appearance of oxygen vacancies with the loss of oxygen atoms is one of the origins of fatigue in PZT due to weakening of the π bonds by remaining electrons of oxygen atoms.

Similar to the model by Brennan, Park and Chadi [151] showed with pseudopotential total energy calculations that a tail-to-tail polarization emerges from atomic relaxation around an oxygen vacancy and that its stability is found to be enhanced by charge trapping. Oxygen vacancies in Ti-O-Ti chains along P (c axis) are more favorable than if they are located in the plane normal to the polarization axis (ab plane). However, the pinning effect from a single oxygen vacancy is small. The area and energy of a tail-to-tail domain wall is minimized by a planar accumulation of charged defects lying perpendicular to the polarization axis. This supports the model of agglomeration of oxygen vacancies. Lo and Chen [152] modeled the influence of oxygen vacancies on the single unit cell level using an Ising Model (statistical approach). They found that the octahedral cage of a perovskite cell is distorted in the presence of an oxygen vacancy which modifies the Hamiltonian of the dipole system. This reduces the probability of the flipping of a dipole as well as the coupling between the neighboring dipoles. The increase of oxygen vacancy concentration at the electrode/thin film interface leads to pinning of nucleation sites which hinders switching.

Mechanics Models

Kim et al. [153] presented a model using a thermodynamical approach of the electromechanical properties and finite element calculations that showed that microcracking can qualitatively explain the decrease of polarization and strain observed in fatigue. The model develops a finite element formulation by partitioning each grain into twelve three-node triangular elements. The junctions of three grains or triple points are the sites of stress concentrations due to material anisotropy. Microcracks are introduced at the triple points where the stress is largest, when the magnitude of the applied AC field reaches its maximum. Microcracks are treated as small cavities filled with air resulting from removing the three triangular elements in junction with the triple point. The system ferroelectric/microcrack can be seen as two capacitances in series. The local electric fields drop at the microcracks and in some grains become too weak to switch the domain system in that grain. The authors calculated that a cracked surface covering 2.5% of the sample cross-section yields a polarization loss of 10%.

Kachaturyan [154] proposed that ferroelectric fatigue in PLZT thin films is an electrical manifestation of the mechanical fatigue caused by piezoelectric strains. He argued that the stress originates from the clamping of the non-piezoelectric substrate on the film and calculated that the induced stress is high enough to induce pure mechanical fatigue of the ferroelectric. The mechanism of mechanical fatigue in PLZT is the build-up of resistance to 90° domain wall motion. As this resistance increases, the accompanied stress is accommodated by plastic deformation, i.e. by formation of dislocations. When the dislocation density reaches a certain threshold, microcracks start to form. The resulting increased resistance to domain wall motion is observed in the electrical measurements as an increase in coercive field. In this scenario, the author predicts an increasing fatigue with decreasing frequency, with increasing temperature for thin films and decreasing temperature for bulk ferroelectrics. He explains the strong effect of electrode material on the fatigue resistance by the electromigration from the electrode material into the ferroelectric. The latter is considered to increase the fatigue rate.

Wang et al. [29] also supported the proposal that fatigue is due to stress-induced damages. Microcracks emanate from local anomalies in the material such as internal voids. Their finite element model predicts stresses/electric fields/strains around a simulated two-dimensional void. It includes modified constitutive equations incorporating the effect of temperature in electromechanical properties. The calculations show that the local polarization switching causes large stress concentration around internal anomalies, which are high enough to induce mechanical fatigue and cracks, similar to Kachaturyan's model. At elevated temperature, the stress is released below the fatigue threshold and the material does not fatigue.

Liu et al. [59] also supported the fact that microcracks are the major cause for ferroelectric fatigue. The intersection of 90° domain walls, where the stress concentration occurs, may be the origin of microcracks, which later develop in macrocracks and result in a fraction of domains which do not response to the applied field. In addition, the authors stress the domain-pinning effect due to migration and accumulation of defects at grain boundaries and domain walls.

Dendrite Growth

Duiker et al. [155] proposed a model of fatigue in ferroelectric memories based on impact ionization (e.g. Ti^{4+} to Ti^{3+} conversion), resulting in dendritic growth of oxygen-deficient filaments from the electrodes. These filaments of enhanced conductivity screen the applied field and reduce the polarization through short-circuiting the grains. A Monte Carlo modelling of the potential in the film leads to a simulation of the dendritic growth during cycling. The model predicts a good fit of the polarization with cycle number. Even though the model predicts a good fit of the polarization decay with the cycle number, this approach has not been reused in later models of fatigue.

Local Imprint

Shur et al. [156] developed an iterative model for local screening based on Kolmogorov-Avrami-Ishibashi theory of switching of ferroelectrics. The model is based on 2D rectangular net cells permitting two opposite signs of P. Two types of wall motion are permitted: linear propagation and edge growth. The switching is divided into two parts: the nucleation of new domains and subsequent growth. The nucleation probability is given by

$$p = \exp \frac{-E_a}{E_{ex} + E_b} \tag{2.24}$$

where E_{ex} is the external field, and E_a is the activation field for nucleation, E_b is the local bias field due to certain defects or clamped domains. The free charges constituting the local bias field are not specified. E_b is modified by each switching cycle because of the slow rearrangement of local charge carriers which screen the uncompensated local remnants of the depolarizing field. E_b increases until it shields the external field beneath the locally required coercive field. The domains become entirely blocked. The fraction of non-switchable domains tends to grow with a certain probability, reducing ΔP. The particularity of this model is that it introduces a time dependence of fatigue. The fatigue rate becomes correlated with the cycling frequency and the relaxation time of screening charges.

A model for fatigue in thin films based on the derivation of macroscopic quantities from the Landau-type thermodynamic potential was published by Ricinschi et al. [157]. The film is regarded as a lattice of interacted Landau units which are attempting to switch under an electric field. The average hysteresis loop is derived by averaging the individual ones. The authors stress the importance for a valid model to yield a good correlated fit of the changes of several macroparameters. The best fit is obtained when considering a fraction of dead ferroelectricity regions with fixed polarization and no switching , even when the external field is swept, and a fraction of weak ferroelectricity regions which experience a modified local field. The origin of the built-in field is believed to be defect charges such as oxygen vacancies created during polarization reversal, responsible for the gradual inhibition of switching at both electrode-PZT interfaces.

2.3.4   Unipolar Fatigue

Only very little research has been published on the effects of unipolar cycling on fer-roelectrics. Unipolar cycling is known to induce a much smaller polarization loss than bipolar cycling. In bulk PLZT 7/56/44, Pan et al. [24] found that the peak of the unipo-lar polarization loop decreased by 15 % after 10^6 unipolar cycles, whereas the height of the bipolar polarization hysteresis loop lost 70% of its initial value after $2 \cdot 10^5$ bipolar cycles. They argued that this difference is due to the fact that there is no energy barrier associated with the change of the intrinsic polarization in the unipolar case, whereas the material has to overcome an energy barrier to reverse the polarization in the bipolar case (see Section 2.1). An increase in this energy barrier is believed to be the origin of bipolar fatigue.

   In PZT thin films, Kholkin et al. [28] observed a small decrease of d_{33} of 15 % after unipolar cycling as well as a shift of the bipolar polarization hysteresis loop in the direction of the cycling field. They attributed this shift to the build-up of an offset field induced by injection and pinning of free charge carriers near the film-electrode interfaces. Chikarmane et al. [158] also found a smaller degradation in unipolar cycled PZT thin films than in bipolar fatigued ones. Furthermore, in both loading modes, the fatigue rate was found to be faster in N_2 annealed films compared to O_2 annealed films.

Chapter 3

Experiment

3.1 Samples

All measurements were performed on a commercial material (PIC 151, PI Ceramic GmbH). The samples were disc shaped and 10 mm in diameter with a thickness of 1 mm. They consisted of material of the ternary phase system $Pb(Ni_{1/3}Sb_{2/3})O_3$ - $PbTiO_3$ - $PbZrO_3$, including about 8% of the $Pb(Ni_{1/3}Sb_{2/3})O_3$ composition in the tetragonal vicinity of the morphotropic phase boundary of PZT. The samples were prepared by the standard mixed oxide route and sintered at 1300 °C for 120 min in ambient atmosphere. The average grain size was about 6 μm [159]. The Curie point given by the manufacturer was 250 °C and was confirmed by own measurements, as will be seen later. All samples were electroded with silver burned into the surface at 850 °C, leaving a rim of 250 μm uncovered in order to avoid dielectric breakdown when applying a high electric field. The samples were unpoled and all stemmed from the same sintering charge. The material properties given by the manufacturer are listed in Table 3.1.

Density [gcm^{-3}]	ϵ_{33}/ϵ_o	$\tan \delta$ (10^{-3})	k_p	d_{33} ($10^{-12}\, m/V$)	T_c (°C)
7.8	2100	15	0.62	450	250

Table 3.1: Properties of poled PIC 151

3.2 Cycling

3.2.1 Bipolar Cycling

The cycling field used was ± 2 kV/mm. Since E_c of the uncycled material was determined
to be about 1 kV/mm, this field represents 2 E_c. The voltage of sinusoidal waveform was
generated by transforming the line voltage (50 Hz, 220V) with a high voltage transformer
(Ulmer Transformatoren). The voltage was regulated between zero and maximum value
using a variable transformer. An ohmic voltage divider 1:1000 was built into the set-up in
the secondary circuit in order to display the cycling voltage on a digital oscilloscope. Each
sample was placed between two copper clamps electrically connected to the power supply.
All samples were immersed in a bath of silicon oil (AK35, Wacker-Chemie GmbH) in order
to avoid arcing and to ensure good thermal conductivity. The cycling field was steadily
increased from zero to the maximum value within 5 seconds. Then the electric field was
held constant for a number of switching cycles N, whereafter the field was reduced to
zero again within 5 seconds. This procedure ensures that the macroscopic polarization of
each sample equals approximately zero after cycling. Finally the samples were removed
from the cycling set-up and the different measuring procedures described beneath were
conducted.

3.2.2 Unipolar Cycling

The unipolar cyclic voltage was generated by extending the set-up with a diode bridge
rectifier (Figure 3.1). The samples were thus cycled at 100 Hz unipolar with a $|\sin(\omega)|$
waveform. Since the impedance of the rectifier is very high in blocking direction, the time
constant of the immediate sample circuit had to be reduced for permitting the sample
at the end of each waveform cycle to discharge. This was achieved by connecting an
additional resistance of 100 Ω in parallel to the samples. For both unipolar and bipolar
cycling, 10 samples could be fatigued at the same time.

3.3 Electrical Measurements

3.3.1 Polarization and Strain Measurements

All data (polarization, field, strain) were simultaneously recorded by the measuring set-
up (AMS, Vallen Systeme GmbH, Figure 3.2) containing an analog-digital converter.
The high voltage (HV) was delivered by a bipolar high voltage power supply (F.u.G.

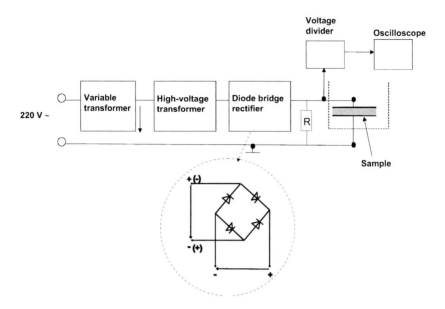

Figure 3.1: Set-up used for unipolar cycling with detail of the diode bridge rectifier.

Elektronik GmbH) driven by a frequency generator (Hewlett Packard). The output of the frequency generator was connected to the AD-converter device and converted to a field value, considering the sample thickness and the amplification of the power supply. The sample was placed in a silicon oil bath in order to avoid arcing. The dielectric hysteresis loops were determined with a Sawyer Tower set-up. A linear capacitor (C = 10 μF $>>$ C$_{sample}$) was placed between the sample and ground. The voltage U on this capacitor was acquired by the AD-converter and converted to polarization considering the measuring capacitance and the surface of the sample electrode. Since the input impedance of the measuring device is only 1 MΩ, an impedance converter with a high impedance operational amplifier (represented in the figure as a resistance R=10$^{12}\Omega$) was included in order to allow a static measurement. Considering the errors due to the leakage charges (in the case of an ohmic leakage current), the geometry of the sample, the measurement capacitance, the error in the polarization measurement was found to be less than 2%.

For the strain hysteresis loops, a linear variable displacement transducer (LVDT, resolution 20 nm, W1T3, Hottinger Baldwin Meßtechnik) was connected to an AC measuring bridge (AB12, MC55, AP01, Hottinger Baldwin Meßtechnik). The metal tip of the transducer was placed onto the upper face of the sample and provided the electric contact

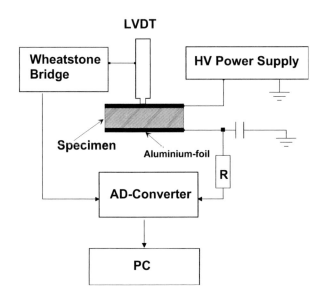

Figure 3.2: Experimental set-up to measure the polarization and strain hysteresis loops

with the sample electrode for the high voltage. The sample was slightly pressed to avoid
oil films between the lower sample electrode and the supporting flat metal piece. One
unipolar cycle was applied to the sample to re-establish the ferroelastically induced error
due to this procedure. The measurement started 5 minutes after this operation to allow
a reproducible relaxation of strain. The analog output signal of the bridge was amplified
with a custom built amplifier by a factor of 20 and acquired by the AD-converter device.
It was then converted to strain, considering the amplification of the signal and the sample
thickness. Considering the thickness of the sample and the resolution of the transducer,
the error in the strain measurement was calculated to be less than 3%. However it must be
considered that the strain measurement, in contrast to the the polarization measurement,
is a local measurement. The strain is acquired where the tip of the LVDT is located on
the surface, whereas the polarization measurement consider the total polarization of the
sample. The results show that the strain may vary on the sample surface (see 5.2.1).

The AMS device was monitored by a computer and the software used for the acquisition and the display of the measured values was AMS3$^{\circledR}$ (Vallen Systeme GmbH). The
bipolar hysteresis loops were recorded by applying a triangular bipolar field of 40mHz
driven to maximal values of $\pm$ 2kV/mm. For the unipolar hysteresis loops the field was
driven between 0 and 2kV/mm at the same frequency.

3.3.2 Fast Switching Measurements

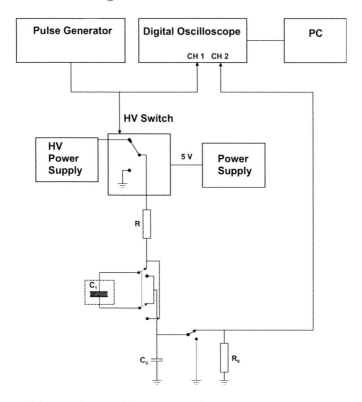

Figure 3.3: Schematic diagram of the experimental set-up to study switching of polarization under application of short DC voltage pulses [160]

The fatigued samples were switched using the experimental set-up shown schematically in Figure 3.3. The DC voltage U=2kV was supplied by a conventional high voltage power supply (F.u.G. Elektronik GmbH, Rosenheim, Germany) buffered by a $0.5\mu F$ high voltage capacitor, capable to support the required current. A drop of silicon oil (AK 1000, Wacker Chemie) was spread on the edge of the sample in order to avoid arcing between both electrodes during the switching. A resistance R was put in series with the sample $(C_s \simeq 1nF)$ in order to limit the maximum current of the poling circuit I_{max}=U/R. The experimental time constant was then determined by $\tau_{max} = R \cdot C_s$. Different resistors and smaller sample sizes were used in order to estimate the intrinsic material time constant, whereafter a resistance R of 100 Ω was used, yielding $\tau \sim 100$ ns. The displacement measurements were conducted by measuring the voltage drop at a capacitance of 4.42 μF in series with the sample. The voltage drop was measured by a digital oscilloscope (TDS 3014, Tektronix), except for very long switching where an electrometer was used (Keithley Instruments). Since the input resistance of the oscilloscope is only 10^6 Ω, an operational amplifier of high input impedance $R_0 = 10^{13}$ Ω was introduced between the measurement capacitance and the oscilloscope in order to avoid charge or voltage loss during the time of measurement.

The switching of the high voltage was performed by means of an electronic high voltage/high current push pull switch (Behlke, Germany) supplied by 5V DC delivered by an external power supply. The switch was driven by a low voltage pulse generator. The form of the applied pulses was rectangular from ground to high voltage and back to ground. Pulses of a duration of 1ms to 100s could be applied. Two channels of the oscilloscope were used. CH 1 was connected to the output of the pulse generator and CH 2 to the measurement capacitance. The acquisition of the measured charge was triggered on CH 1 with a signal of 5V. A special switch permitted the measurement capacitor to discharge after each acquisition in order to avoid DC offsets during further measurements. Since the HV power supply could only deliver a unipolar voltage, an additional switch was used to apply this voltage either to the upper or to the bottom electrode in order to reverse the polarization. The charge curves were acquired on the oscilloscope and exported to a PC equipped with the software Labview®(National Instruments Corporation). The displacement values were calculated considering measuring capacitance and the surface of the sample electrode.

Because of the limited sampling rate of the oscilloscope, several polarization reversals were performed in order to cover several orders of magnitude in time. After bipolar cycling, each sample was first poled for one hour at 2kV (2 E_c) and relaxed for one hour before measurement. The unipolar cycled samples were not poled since they were cycled in one direction, but the measurement started at least one hour after cycling finished in order to allow charge relaxation. The measurement sequence was as followed: after cycling (and poling in the bipolar case), each sample was switched for 1ms, then poled for 100s, switched for 1s, poled for 100s, switched for 100s, poled for 100s, switched for one hour.

3.4   Impedance Spectroscopy

Impedance spectroscopy (IS) is a powerful method to investigate the microstructure of a material. IS involves a small AC field ($\sim$100mV) which is applied to the system over a wide range of frequencies (10^{-3}-10^7Hz). The response is a composite of the different electroactive regions within the material. The advantage of IS over conventional DC techniques lies in the possibility of characterizing inhomogeneous materials. Each electroactive region shows a characteristic resistance R and a capacitance C. The product RC gives the relaxation time or time constant which is characteristic for each region. Different regions will relax at different frequencies according to:

$$\omega_{max} \ R \ C = 1 \tag{3.1}$$

Thus each electroactive region may be characterized by its resistive and capacitive behavior. There are several measurement methods available to measure the impedance [161]. The method used in this work is the bridge method (see measurements).

3.4.1 Basics

The Complex Impedance

In DC theory, the resistance R is a scalar defined by Ohms law R=V/I. Analogous, for AC:

$$Z - \frac{V_0}{I_0} \tag{3.2}$$

where V_0 and I_0 are the voltage and current amplitude and Z is defined as the impedance. Unless the sample behaves as a perfect resistor, under AC voltage there will be a phase difference θ between the applied voltage and the resulting current. Impedance is a vector which can be expressed as a complex number.

$$Z^* = Z' - j \ Z'' \tag{3.3}$$

Formalisms

The most common method of plotting impedance data is in the form of Z^* plots. However, other formalisms can be used:

$$\text{Admittance} \qquad Y^* = Y' + j \ Y'' = \frac{1}{Z^*} \tag{3.4}$$

$$\text{Permittivity} \qquad \epsilon^* = \epsilon' - j \ \epsilon'' = \frac{1}{M^*} \tag{3.5}$$

$$\text{Electric Modulus} \qquad M^* = M' + j \ M'' = j \ \omega \ C_0 \ Z^* \tag{3.6}$$

where ω is the angular frequency and C_0 is the vacuum capacitance of the measurement cell. $C_0 = \varepsilon_0/k$, where k is the cell constant and ε_0 the permittivity of free space,

$8.854 \cdot 10^{-14}$F/cm. All four formalisms are inter-related and highlight different processes or electroactive regions of the same system. This will be illustrated by an example in the data analysis section.

Simple Elements

For the three basic electric elements it follows

$$\text{ideal resistor:}\quad Z^* = Z' = R \quad (\theta = 0) \tag{3.7}$$

$$\text{ideal capacitor:}\quad Z^* = -j\, Z'' = 1/j\omega C \quad (\theta = +90) \tag{3.8}$$

$$\text{ideal inductor:}\quad Z^* = -j\, Z'' = j\omega L \quad (\theta = -90) \tag{3.9}$$

The combination of R and C elements in series yields:

$$Z^* = R - j\omega C \tag{3.10}$$

The combination of R and C elements in parallel yields:

$$Z^* = R/(1 + (\omega RC)^2) + j\, R[(\omega RC)/(1 + (\omega RC)^2)] \tag{3.11}$$

$$Z'' = R[DP] \tag{3.12}$$

The term in square brackets in Z'' is the mathematical expression of a Debye peak (DP). The complex impedance Z^* gives rise to a semi-circle. The frequency at the semi-circle maximum ω_{max} and correspondingly at the Debye peak maximum is given by:

$$\omega_{max} = \frac{1}{RC} \tag{3.13}$$

Data Analysis

The data analysis follows from modelling experimental data with equivalent circuits, i.e. a combination of simple elements [163]. A common circuit for ceramics is composed by two RC elements (R and C in parallel) in series. One element corresponds to the bulk of the material, the other to the grain boundaries (Figure 3.4). Usually $R_{gb} > R_b$ and $C_{gb} > C_b$. With such a series circuit it is desirable to separate both RC elements and extract their R and C values. Both spectroscopic and complex plane plots can be used to extract the resistance and capacitance of each region. This is best achieved by using a combination of both Z and M formalisms. For both RC elements in series, the following equations can be obtained :

$$Z'' = R_b \cdot [\text{bulk DP}] + R_{gb} \cdot [\text{gb DP}] \tag{3.14}$$

$$M'' = \frac{C_0}{C_b} \cdot [\text{bulk DP}] + \frac{C_0}{C_b} \cdot [\text{gb DP}] \tag{3.15}$$

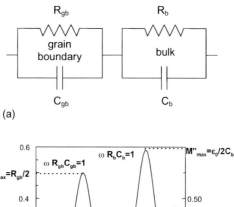

(a)

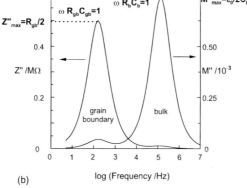

(b)

Figure 3.4: a) Typical equivalent circuit for analysis of ceramics where $R_{gb} > R_b$ b) combined Z'', M'' spectra for the circuit in a) (after correction for the sample geometry) . From [162].

The response of this circuit in a spectroscopic plot is shown in Figure 3.4 b). The magnitude of the Debye peaks scales according to R for Z'' spectra and C^{-1} for M'' spectra.

$$Z''_{max} = \frac{R}{2} \qquad M''_{max} = \frac{C_0}{2C} \qquad (3.16)$$

Consequently Z'' (and Z^* plots) spectra are dominated by large R elements whereas M'' spectra (and M^* plots) are dominated by small C elements. The maxima of the peaks occur according to Equation (3.13). The time constant and therefore the frequency of the peak maximum f_{max} is an intrinsic property of the RC element since it depends on its geometry. In the complex planes, each RC element gives rise to a semi-circle (Figure 3.5) as mentioned above. Thus, accurate values of R and C can be calculated from the intercepts in the complex plane plots. The values can also be estimated from the peak-height in the spectroscopic plots M'' and Z''. Usually regions of low capacitance such as the interior of the grains are characterized using the M formalism, whereas regions

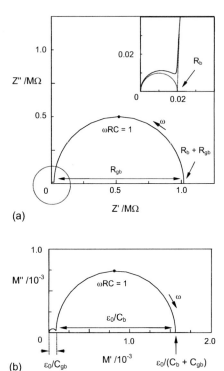

(a)

(b)

Figure 3.5: Z^* and M^* plots in the complex planes for the circuit in Figure 3.4 (after correction for the sample geometry). From [162].

of high resistivity such as the grain boundaries are characterized using the Z formalism. Considering that, in the example presented here, $R_{gb} > R_b$ and $C_{gb} > C_b$, R_{gb} can be extracted from the Z^* plot and C_b from the M^* plot. From the position of the peak maxima in the spectroscopic plots, ω_{max}[bulk DP] and ω_{max}[gb DP] can be evaluated, and from the equation 3.13, C_{gb} and R_{gb} can be derived. This example stresses the relevance of combining illustrations of the results in the different formalisms.

It is of course possible to find other responses which correspond to further electroactive regions i.e. an interface layer or a second phase or heterogeneities in the material.

3.4.2 Measurements

The measurements were conducted at the University of Cambridge and at the Darmstadt University of Technology. The two experimental set-ups were similar and are schematically illustrated in Figure 3.6. The sample was placed in the furnace and the sample electrodes contacted with Pt electrodes, which were further connected to the impedance analyzer via screened BNC cables. The temperature in the furnace was monitored by a Eurotherm temperature controller. A thermocouple was placed in direct proximity to the sample in order to monitor its temperature. The impedance analyzers (HP 4192A in Cambridge and HP4284A, HP4285A in Darmstadt, Hewlett Packard) were connected to a computer for the data acquisition and analysis. These devices use the auto-balancing bridge method. A Wheatstone bridge is used, in which variable R and C are balanced at each frequency until the current flow through the detector is zero. The value of the unknown impedance is then calculated from the other impedances of the bridge. Two types

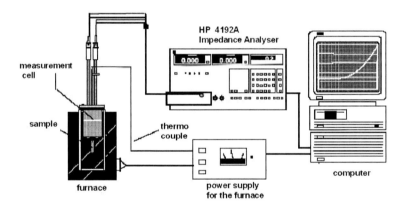

Figure 3.6: Set-up for the impedance measurement

of measurement were conducted. Measurements of the dielectric constant at 10^4 and 10^5 Hz over a range of temperatures between room temperature and 600 °C (heating and cooling) under ambient atmosphere were carried out for virgin and fatigued samples. The applied AC voltage was 100 mV. The heating and cooling rates were slow (1 °C/min) in order to achieve a thermal equilibrium in the furnace so that the temperature measured by the thermoelement matches the sample temperature. The acquisition were conducted with steps of 1 °C. Samples with different fatigue states were measured. Before measurement, each sample was poled one hour at 2 E_c (2 kV/mm). In a second set of measurements, frequency spectra (5Hz-13MHz) of samples with different cycle numbers were acquired at different temperatures from -150 °C to 600 °C. These measurements were intended to observe the relaxation processes occurring in the material relative to its fatigue state. Data analysis was carried out using a combination of in-house software and Zview® (Version 1.5, Scribner Associates). All data were corrected for sample geometry and plotted in the different formalisms. After each heating/cooling step, measurements were started when the capacitance reached a stable value, indicating the thermal equilibrium in the sample.

3.5   Visible-Near Infrared Reflectance Spectroscopy

Measurements of visible-near infrared spectroscopy were carried out on samples with different cycling modes and fatigue states. The samples were ground off down to half of their thickness and polished with different grain sizes down to 1 μm according to the polishing program described in [164]. Since the samples are opaque, a certain scattering of the light was expected, thus the method used was the reflectance spectroscopy. Diffuse Reflectance Spectroscopy (DRS), also known as Elastic Scattering Spectroscopy, is a non-invasive technique that uses the interaction of light, absorption and scattering, to produce a characteristic reflectance spectrum.

Photons are absorbed in materials by several electronic and vibrational processes. Theses processes, such as crystal field effects, charge transfer, color centers, transition to the conduction band and overtone and combination tone vibrational transition and their wavelength dependence, allow the derivation of information about the chemistry of a material from its reflected light [165].

Diffuse reflection is dependent not only on absorption and the absorption coefficient K, but also on the structure of the sample surface and its strew, included as the strew coefficient S. A mathematical relationship exists between these constants and the reflectance signal R_{diff}. The proportionality is described in the Kubelka-Munk function

$$\alpha = \frac{K}{S} = \frac{(1 - R_{diff})^2}{2R_{diff}} \tag{3.17}$$

Figure 3.7 shows the schematic geometry of the reflectance measurements. A deuterium lamp was used to generate the light in the ultraviolet region up to 319.2 nm and a xenon lamp for the visible and infrared region. The frequency was set by a grating monochromator. The incident beam was reflected at the surface of the polished sample and reflected light was emitted and equal in all directions. In an integrating sphere (Ulbrich sphere) made of 100% reflecting material (Labsphere®), all the reflected intensity was ultimately

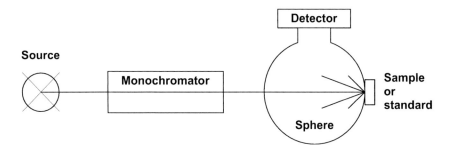

Figure 3.7: Schematic set-up for the reflectance measurement

collected at the detector. Two types of detectors were used: a photomultiplier for the ultraviolet and visible region up to 860 nm and a PbS cell for the infrared region. The spectrometer used for the measurement was the UV/VIS/NIR spectrometer Lambda 900 from Perkin Elmer (Perkin Elmer Corporation) and was connected to a computer for data acquisition. The software used was UV900Lab® (Perkin Elmer corporation). Since the set-up yields a distribution in intensity depending on wavelength, a standard sample of the same material as the Ulbrich sphere (Labsphere®) was first measured and used as a reference (100% reflectivity). The reflectance of the samples was then calculated relative to the intensity reflected by the standard.

3.6 Thermal Annealing

The effect of thermal annealing on unipolar cycled samples was studied with polarization and strain hysteresis loops. Bipolar cycled samples were characterized after thermal annealing with fast-switching and impedance spectroscopy measurements. In each case, for the hysteresis loops and switching measurements, the samples were short circuited in order to allow the rearrangement of charge carriers between the electrodes during the depolarization. They were then placed in an oven under ambient atmosphere, heated at a ramp of 8 °C/min, held at maximum temperature for three hours, and cooled at approximatively 3 °C/min. Consecutive annealing steps were performed on each sample and the sample was characterized after each step in order to avoid scattering effects from different samples. For the impedance spectroscopy measurements, the bipolar cycled samples were measured at high temperatures, so an acquisition was made directly after the temperature reached the annealing temperature (600 °C) and successive acquisitions after one hour and two hours at this temperature.

3.7   High-Field Treatment

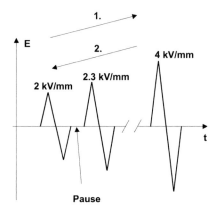

Figure 3.8: Profile of the high-field treatment at low frequency applied after unipolar cycling. The bipolar triangular field was increased (1) and reduced (2) in discrete steps.

After unipolar cycling, the bipolar polarization and strain hysteresis loops were measured as described in Section 3.3.1 but at higher fields. A hysteresis loop with a bipolar triangular field of ±2kV at 40mHz was first recorded, and after a short pause the height of the field was increased and a new cycle measured and so forth. Consecutive hysteresis loops were recorded at increasing fields from ±2kV/mm up to ±4kV/mm (±4E_c) and reduced once again to ±2kV/mm as displayed in Figure 3.8.

3.8   Re-Electroding

The influence of the near electrode region on bipolar fatigue was investigated by polishing the fatiguing electrodes after cycling and successive polarization, fast-switching and impedance spectroscopy measurements. The polarization and strain hysteresis loops of a unipolar cycled sample were also acquired before and after re-electroding. After cycling, the initial electrodes were polished (around 20μm on both sides) with SiC powder and diamond paste with different grain sizes down to 1μm according to the polishing program described in [164]. New electrodes were painted with silver paste and dried at 70° C in an air chamber before measurement.

Chapter 4

Results

This section is divided into two parts. The measurements after unipolar cycling will be first presented and following these, the measurements concerning the effects of bipolar cycling.

4.1 Unipolar Fatigue

4.1.1 Bipolar Measurements

Bipolar hysteresis loops were recorded after unipolar cycling in order to observe the effect of unipolar cycling on the switching behavior of the material. A direct comparison of the polarization and strain hysteresis is given in Figure 4.1. The polarization hysteresis shows a very slight decrease in remanent polarization. The first hysteresis loop is shifted to the left and the following ones run on about the same track with a small continuous shift of the entire hysteresis to lower polarization values. For each sample, the strain hysteresis after cycling always exhibits an asymmetry in the same direction, that is, the strain reached in the cycling direction corresponding to the right wing (S_r) of the hysteresis loop is always higher than in the opposite direction (left wing S_l). As for the polarization hysteresis, the first loop deviates from the following ones. In the subsequent hysteresis loops, a continuous increase of S_r and an decrease of S_l is observed. Thus consecutive bipolar cycles yield a gradual reduction of the strain asymmetry of a cycled sample.

In Figures 4.2-4.4 the parameters obtained from the bipolar hysteresis loops are shown between 0 and $4.13 \cdot 10^8$ cycles. The parameters of the third polarization and strain hysteresis were evaluated because the first loop is not complete and differs from the following ones. The results were then averaged on three samples. According to Figure 4.2,

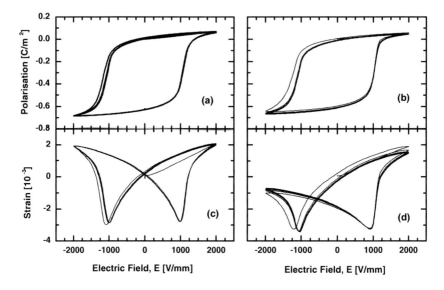

Figure 4.1: Bipolar polarization hysteresis a) before and after b) unipolar cycling $(3.2 \cdot 10^8$ cycles). The first five cycles are shown. c) and d) are the corresponding strain hysteresis loops.

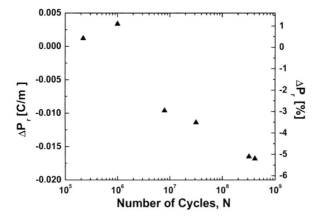

Figure 4.2: Reduction of switchable polarization due to unipolar cycling. The change of the total height of the hysteresis, $\Delta(2P_r)/2$, is plotted versus cycle number.

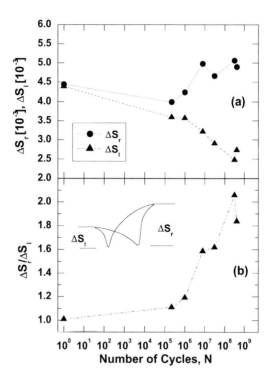

Figure 4.3: a) Strain amplitudes of the right (r) and left (l) wings of the strain hysteresis loops. b) Ratio of the right to left strain amplitudes.

the remanent polarization decreases steadily with cycle number. However, the decrease in P_r is small, reaching only 5.2 % of P_r after $4.2 \cdot 10^8$ cycles in comparison to the degradation induced by bipolar fatigue of around 70 %.

In Figure 4.3, the strain values S_r, S_l and their ratio are shown. It is obvious that the asymmetry of the strain hysteresis increases with cycle number. Although the increase of the right wing is not as evident as the decrease of the left wing, the ratio, taken as a measure of the asymmetry, increases steadily with unipolar cycle number. Figure 4.4 shows the shift of the coercive field with cycle number averaged for both polarities, evaluated from the polarization hysteresis (Figure 4.4 a) (linear regression at P=0) and from the strain hysteresis (Figure 4.4 b) (strain minima). With cycle number, the coercive fields are slightly shifted to lower values. However, the shift observed in the polarization hysteresis is smaller than the shift of the strain hysteresis, here determined from the

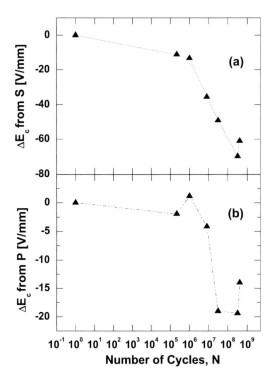

Figure 4.4: Relative shift of the coercive fields plotted as the shift of the center between the left and right values as determined a) from the minimum of the strain hysteresis, and b) from the polarization hysteresis.

minimum in the butterfly-loops (-19.4 V/mm after $3.2 \cdot 10^8$ cycles against -69.8 V/mm for the strain hysteresis).

4.1.2   Unipolar Measurements

In Figure 4.5, the unipolar polarization and strain hysteresis are shown before cycling a), b) and after cycling, in the cycling direction c), d), and in the opposite direction e), f). The polarization hysteresis loops show a very slight decrease in slope in both directions after cycling. The slope of the strain hysteresis in cycling direction has increased, whereas it has decreased in the opposite direction. It is more relevant to notice the differences between consecutive hysteresis measurements. For the polarization as for the strain of the

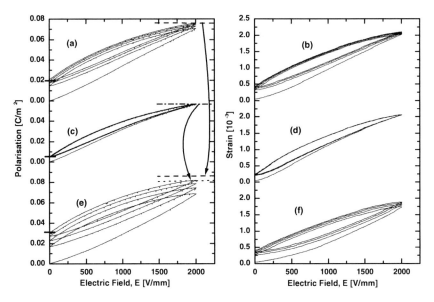

Figure 4.5: Minor polarization (left) and strain (right) hysteresis loops measured a), b) before unipolar cycling, c), d) after $4.1 \cdot 10^8$ unipolar fatigue cycles, and e), f) at opposite polarity after a single step of polarization inversion. In order to illustrate the relative change of the strain amplitude, identical bottom markers are introduced on the left hand side of the plots. The markers on the right-hand side indicate the differences in slope.

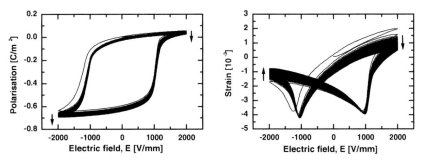

Figure 4.6: Bipolar measurement cycles after $3.2 \cdot 10^8$ unipolar fatigue cycles. a) Polarization, and b) strain. 200 measuring cycles are shown.

uncycled sample, consecutive hysteresis loops steadily shift to higher strain or polarization values, respectively. These shifts almost disappear after cycling in the cycling direction.

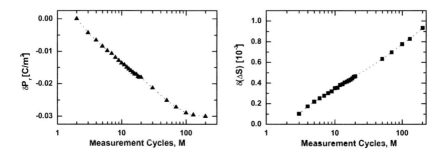

Figure 4.7: a) Reduction of the center of the polarization hysteresis loop measured as the average of the $+P_r$ and $-P_r$ corresponding to Figure 4.6. b) Reduction of the maximum strain at 2 kV/mm as a function of measurement cycle number.

Upon polarity inversion, a second set of unipolar measuring cycles was applied to the samples. The relative shift of these hysteresis cycles at inverted polarity was significantly larger than before and even more so than after unipolar cycling, indicating the relevance of relaxational behavior.

4.1.3 Multiple Bipolar Measurement Cycles

200 bipolar hysteresis loops after unipolar cycling are shown in Figure 4.6. The arrows indicate the shift directions of the consecutive loops. A shift of the polarization hysteresis to lower polarization values is observed for both the positive and negative polarity, expressing a shift of the hysteresis loop as a whole. The strain measurements exhibit a steady removal of the asymmetry with a decrease of the right wing and an increase of the left wing of the hysteresis loop. After 200 bipolar cycles, the asymmetry is not yet completely removed. As shown in Figure 4.7, the shifts of both hysteresis loops show a logarithmic dependency on the number of measurement cycles.

4.1.4 Bipolar Measurements under High Electric Fields

After the fatigue procedure, the applied maximum fields were raised in discrete steps as described in 3.7. Figure 4.8 shows the evolution of the bipolar polarization, strain and electrostrictive hysteresis loops with increasing field and subsequent decreasing field. At twice the cycling field (4 E_c), the polarization hysteresis grows back to its unfatigued value (2 P_r=0.68 C/m^2, Figure 4.8 a). The observed shift of the center of the hysteresis is a true effect and not an experimental artefact. Along with the polarization, the strain

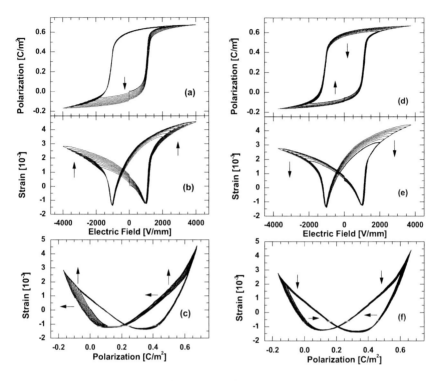

Figure 4.8: Bipolar a) polarization b) strain and c) electrostrictive hysteresis for rising electric fields after $3.2 \cdot 10^8$ unipolar fatigue cycles at 2 kV/mm. d) Polarization, e) strain, and f) electrostrictive hysteresis for subsequently decreasing electric fields.

amplitude rises to $6 \cdot 10^{-3}$ peak to peak at $2\,E_c$ hardly becoming more symmetric for rising fields (Figure 4.8 b). The electrostrictive hysteresis (Figure 4.8 c) links the polarization and strain hysteresis. In a subsequent set of cycles, the maximum field was reduced step by step to the fatigue cycling field value. At this point, the center point of the polarization hysteresis remained identical during all cycles (Figure 4.8 d). The strain hysteresis then dropped back to small values at lower fields after the high field treatment, but the asymmetry was mostly maintained (Figure 4.8 e).

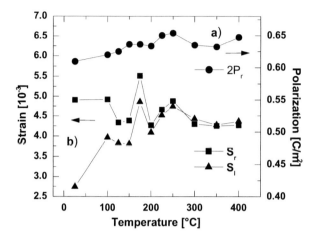

Figure 4.9: Development of a) the remanent polarization and b) the maximum strain amplitude of a unipolar cycled sample ($8 \cdot 10^6$ cycles) at room temperature after different annealing treatments at the temperatures indicated .

4.1.5   Measurements after Thermal Annealing

Bipolar hysteresis loops were recorded after unipolar cycling and thermal annealing. Figure 4.9 displays the evolution of the remanent polarization (Figure 4.9 a) and of both wings of the strain hysteresis after the consecutive annealing steps (Figure 4.9 b). The fairly high scattering of the strain values comes from the fact that the strain hysteresis loops were acquired at different locations on the electrode for each measurement (see 3.3.1). However, it can be clearly observed that the asymmetry of the strain hysteresis is almost completely removed after a single heat treatment at 100 °C and completely vanishes above 250 °C, occurring at significantly lower temperatures than in the bipolar case [130]. The very slight decrease of polarization after cycling is also very quickly recovered.

4.1.6   Fast Switching Measurement

The time dependent polarization switching of two unipolar cycled samples is shown in Figure 4.10 in comparison to a fresh sample. The samples were switched in the opposite direction of cycling. It can be observed that a retardation occurs in the polarization switching which increases with cycle number. The retardation is much smaller than after bipolar fatigue (see Section 4.2.1). This correlates with the polarization and hysteresis loop measurements (see Section 4.1.1). However, it can be seen that the reduction of

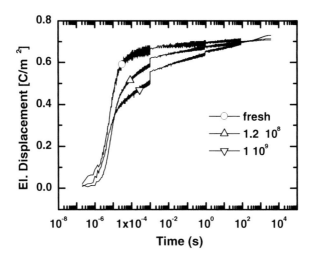

Figure 4.10: Switching data after subtraction of the leakage current at two stages of unipolar cycling (cycle numbers as indicated).

polarization is greater for the fast switching components than for the slow components. Whereas the polarization loss is 5% at 10s, corresponding to the frequency at which the precedent hysteresis loops were measured, it reaches 30 % at 10^{-4}s. Steps can be observed at 10^{-3}s and 1s, the time bases at which the subsequent switchings were conducted. This is due to the fact that the samples were switched and poled again in the cycling direction several times. As was observed above a bipolar field has a recovery effect on a unipolar cycled sample. Thus the measurement procedure is only completely reliable for the first switching during 1ms.

Figure 4.11 displays successive polarization reversals of 1ms in the opposite direction of cycling (switch 1) and back in the cycling direction (switch 2), followed by similar switchings of 1s (switch 3 and 4) for a unipolar cycled sample($1 \cdot 10^9$ cycles). The first switching shows a retardation as in Figure 4.10, but the same amount of polarization is reversed back in the cycling direction as quickly as in a fresh sample, which indicates that the first reversal changed the switching state of the sample. The same effect occurs if the sample is switched for 1s.

If the sample is switched for one hour, the switching behavior is completely recovered. The switching is as fast as in a fresh sample and the strain hysteresis loop shows no asymmetry anymore.

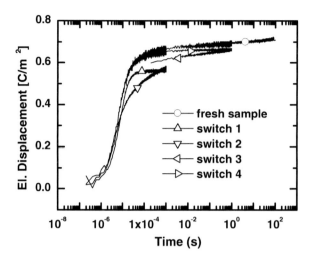

Figure 4.11: Successive switchings after unipolar cycling ($1 \cdot 10^9$ cycles) for 1ms (switch 1 and 2) and for 1s (switch 3 and 4)

4.1.7   Re-Electroding

Figure 4.12 displays the polarization and strain hysteresis loops after unipolar cycling ($4.2 \cdot 10^7$ cycles) and after the polishing and re-electroding of the sample. The strain measured after re-electroding is higher, but the asymmetry observed after cycling remains relatively constant after re-electroding. The ratio of the height of the right wing over the left wing of the butterfly curve is 1.26 after cycling and 1.19 after re-electroding.

4.2   Bipolar Fatigue

4.2.1   Fast Switching Measurements

Figure 4.13 shows the polarization build-up during switching for different cycle numbers after bipolar fatigue. The high increase of the measured charge for an extended period of time is due to the leakage current (surface and bulk), which becomes important relative to the polarization build-up. The leakage current was assumed to be of ohmic nature and was fitted linearly for long time (>2000s) and subtracted from the measured charge in order to get the real polarization.

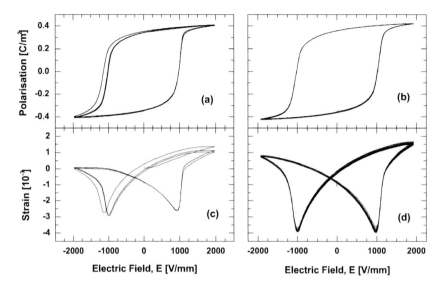

Figure 4.12: Polarization and strain hysteresis loops (a) and (c) of a sample after unipolar cycling ($4.2 \cdot 10^7$ cycles) and after re-electroding (b) and (d)

Figure 4.14 displays the corrected polarization data. Polarization switching is highly retarded in bipolar cycled lead zirconate titanate. One component, P_{fast}, switches at the time constant of the electrical circuitry and thus represents domain switching processes faster than the extrinsic time constant. A second contribution, P_{slow}, is strongly delayed.

Figure 4.15 shows the relaxation for a variation of the serial resistance and a smaller sample size. The serial resistance of 100 Ω yielded the most reproducible measurements across all time scales used. Unlike an ideal capacitor, the time constants are not reduced proportional to the external resistors (Figure 4.15). This deviation is caused by the intrinsic time constant which was determined to be in the range of 10ns and thus close to values reported for thin films.

During the cyclic fatigue process, all of the fast switching finally converts to slow switching (Figure 4.16). This slow component (Figure 4.17) extends to extremely long time ranges as compared to the usually encountered relaxation in ferroelectrics. Among the different stretched exponential functions available, the simple Kohlrausch-Williams-Watts relation

$$P_{slow} = P^*[1 - exp-(\frac{t}{\tau})^{\beta}] \tag{4.1}$$

proved to yield the best fit, where τ is a characteristic time constant and β (included in

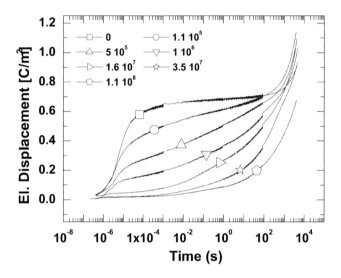

Figure 4.13: Switching data dependent on time for different fatigue states (cycle numbers as indicated)

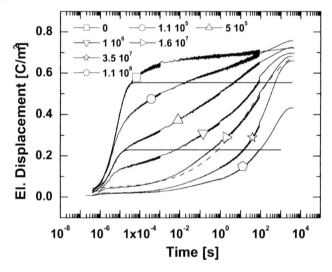

Figure 4.14: Switching data after subtraction of the leakage current at different stages of cycling (cycle numbers as indicated). Fits to the fast switching component are shown in two cases (0 and $5 \cdot 10^5$ cycles) and one global fit (dashed line for $1.6 \cdot 10^7$ cycles).

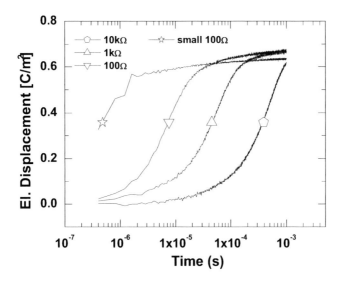

Figure 4.15: Switching data for different serial resistances and a smaller sample size (1/10 of original).

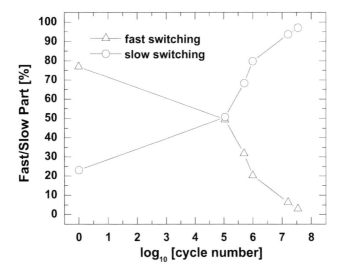

Figure 4.16: Fraction of slow P* and fast switching polarization $P_{f,max}$, $(P^* + P_{f,max} = P_{max})$ at different fatigue stages.

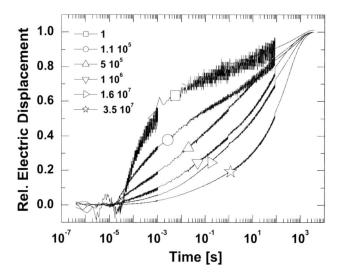

Figure 4.17: Polarization relaxation for the slow switching component normalized to P^*.

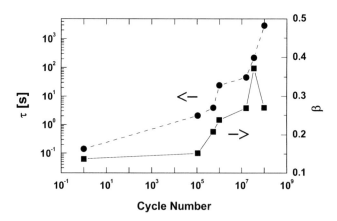

Figure 4.18: Fatigue dependent fitting parameters for a simple stretched exponential function.

the interval [0,1])the so called stretching exponent. First, the slow component was fitted in order to yield a good starting value for the fast switching component, after which the global function $P_{slow} + P_{fast}$ was fitted. For all data sets, an excellent fit is achieved up to 10^3 seconds, which can hardly be discerned from the measured data. The fitting which most deviated from an actual measurement occurred for $3.5 \cdot 10^7$ cycles and is provided in the plot as the worst case. All other fits are omitted for better clarity. The curvature at long times is also reproduced for cycle numbers lower than $1.6 \cdot 10^7$ cycles. Approximately the identical $P_{max} = (P_{fast} + P_{slow}) = 0.68$ C/m^2 $\pm$ 0.05 C/m^2 results from the fits, which means that essentially all polarization is finally achieved, albeit highly delayed.

For the higher cycle numbers, the leakage current exceeds the relaxation current and the saturation values cannot be determined precisely. While this error is still relatively small for $3.5 \cdot 10^7$ cycles (0.05 C/m^2), it cannot be completely excluded, that some polarization is completely clamped for 10^8 cycles. The determination of values for β and τ at this time is therefore not as robust. For 10^8 cycles, P_{max} was also set to 0.68 C/m^2. A different fit could be produced for a lower value of β, but previous data showed that almost all polarization can be recovered thermally without annealing of microcracks [130]. The assumption of the same final value for P_{max} for all cycle numbers thus seems reasonable. Figure 4.18 shows the resulting evolution of the time constant τ and relaxation exponent β with cycle number.

4.2.2 Impedance Spectroscopy

The temperature dependence of the permittivity of a fresh and bipolar fatigued sample ($3 \cdot 10^7$ cycles) is shown in Figure 4.19. Both samples were poled prior to measurement. The room temperature permittivity of the fresh sample is around 1600 at room temperature compared to 800 in the fatigued sample. The virgin sample shows very little hysteresis and exhibits a permittivity maximum, ε'_{max} of ca. 27000 at $T_c \approx 233\,^{\circ}$C. In contrast, the fatigued sample shows a much lower ε'_{max}, of only ca. 2100 at $T_c \approx 250\,^{\circ}$C, an order of magnitude lower than in the fresh sample (Figure 4.19 a). The fatigued sample exhibits significant hysteresis with ε'_{max}, increasing to ca. 3150 at T_c of 239 $^{\circ}$C on cooling (Figure 4.19 b).

Impedance spectroscopy was carried out in the temperature range from -150 $^{\circ}$C to 600 $^{\circ}$C. Data at temperatures < 300 $^{\circ}$C revealed no features attributed to relaxation processes in either fresh or fatigued samples. At high temperature, > 300°C (above T_c), a single relaxation was observed in the data obtained from the fresh sample. A combined Z", M" spectroscopic plot at 568 $^{\circ}$C for a fresh sample indicates a single Debye-like peak which dominates both formalisms (Figure 4.20 a). The associated capacitance of this response

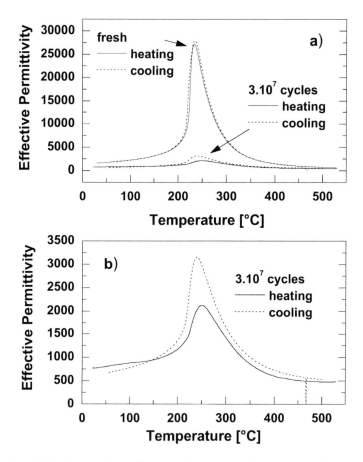

Figure 4.19: a) Permittivity data as function of temperature (heating and cooling) for a fresh and a fatigued sample ($3 \cdot 10^7$ cycles). b) Magnification of the permittivity data of the fatigued sample.

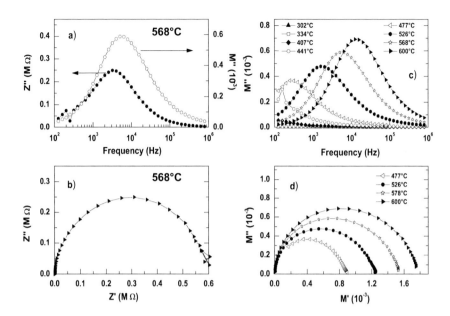

Figure 4.20: Impedance spectroscopy data for a fresh sample expressed as combined Z", M" spectroscopic plot, (a), and Z* complex plane at 568 °C (b). Also, M" spectroscopic (c) and M* complex plane (d) plots as a function of temperature.

was estimated from the M" peak height, M"$_{max}$, using the relation C $= \varepsilon_0/(2$M"$_{max})$ and at 568 °C was estimated as 78pFcm^{-1} and was attributed to the bulk response of the ferroelectric. A more conventional Z* plot is shown in Figure 4.20 b) and indicates a single semicircular arc. The capacitance associated with the bulk response also exhibited Curie-Weiss like behavior consistent with PZT at this temperature: Figure 4.20 c) shows the increase in M"$_{max}$ (decrease in capacitance) with increasing temperature. The complex plane, M* plot is shown in Figure 4.20 d) indicating a single semicircular arc which has an increasing radius with increasing temperature consistent with the decrease in capacitance.

A combined Z", M" spectroscopic plot at 578 °C for a fatigued sample (10^8 cycles) is shown in Figure 4.21 a). The Z" data again shows a single Debye-like peak, and a single semicircular arc in Z*, Figure 4.21 b). The magnitude of the capacitance associated with this response and its temperature dependence was almost identical to that of the fresh sample and again was attributed to the bulk response of PZT. The M" data, however, clearly indicate the presence of a second response as a shoulder on the high frequency side of the main, bulk response peak. M" data over the temperature range 300-600 °C

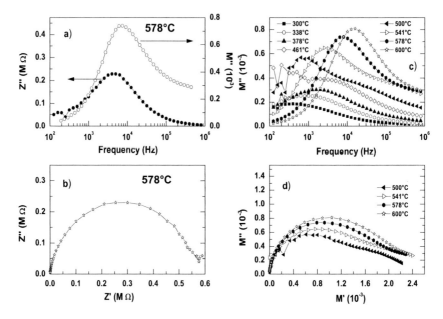

Figure 4.21: Impedance spectroscopy data for a fatigued sample (10^8 cycles) expressed as combined Z", M" spectroscopic plot, (a), and Z^* complex plane at 568 °C (b). Also, M" spectroscopic (c) and M^* complex plane (d) plots as a function of temperature.

clearly shows the presence of this second response (Figure 4.21 c). At high temperature, the bulk peak shows an asymmetry due to the presence of the smaller second response at higher frequency. Correspondingly, the M^* plot is dominated by a large semicircular arc at low frequency attributed to the bulk response, with an additional smaller, partially resolved semicircular arc at higher frequency (Figure 4.21 d). The lower peak height of the high frequency response indicates the existence in fatigued samples of an additional electroactive region with a higher effective capacitance than the bulk. The capacitance extracted from the peak height at 400 °C lies around 150pFcm^{-1}. It is not possible to extract a value at higher temperature because of the overlap of the bulk peak. Both peaks also show a different rate of shift in frequency with temperature indicating different activation energies. The frequency of the peak maximum for the bulk follows an Arrhenius law with activation energy of ∼1.7eV, which corresponds to half of the band gap in PZT. The activation energy of the high frequency peak can only be approximated to be in the range 0.35-0.65eV because of the poor resolution of the peak. In the Z" and Z^* data, only a single response can be observed in both fresh and fatigued samples (Figures 4.20 a-b

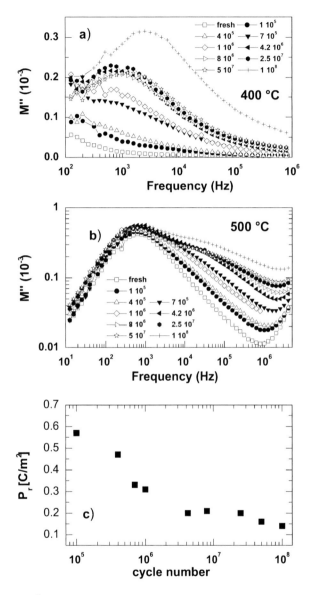

Figure 4.22: : a) M$''$ spectroscopic plot of samples with different cycle number at 400 °C, b) at 500 °C. c) Remanent polarization determined from the dielectric hysteresis loop as function of cycling.

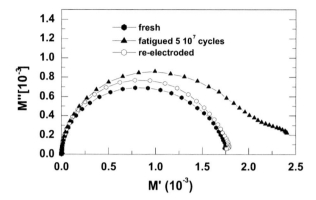

Figure 4.23: M* plot of a fresh, as well as a fatigued sample ($5 \cdot 10^7$ cycles) and of the same fatigued sample after re-electroding.

and 4.21 a-b) and is attributed to the bulk response of the PZT. The additional, fatigue induced response at high frequency is too small to be observed in the Z formalism. Thus the corresponding electroactive region must have a much lower resistivity than the bulk.

M" data at 400 °C shows the change of the fatigue induced response as a function of cycle number (Figure 4.22 a). With increasing cycle number, the peak increases in height and moves to higher frequency. The increase in peak height indicates a decrease in the effective capacitance associated with the fatigue-induced response, and the shift to higher frequency would suggest an increase in the associated conductivity. Similar data at 500 °C show both bulk and fatigue induced responses (Figure 4.22 b). The bulk peak at ca. 600 Hz dominates the M" data in all samples, however the second, high frequency response becomes increasingly obvious with increasing cycle number. The increasing influence of this fatigue induced response to the capacitive behavior of the sample correlates well with the loss in remnant polarization with increasing cycle numbers (Figure 4.22 c) except for the most fatigued sample ($1 \cdot 10^8$ cycles). While the loss of remanent polarization between $5 \cdot 10^7$ cycles and 10^8 cycles is low, a fairly high increase of the high frequency peak is observed.

Interestingly, the effective capacitance extracted from the fatigue induced peak exhibits a Curie-Weiss behavior with temperature, as well as the bulk peak, but with a different Curie constant (not shown).

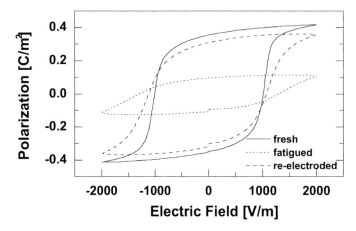

Figure 4.24: Dielectric hysteresis loops of a fresh, as well as a fatigued sample $(3.5 \cdot 10^7$ cycles) and of the same fatigued sample after polishing the near electrode region and re-electroding.

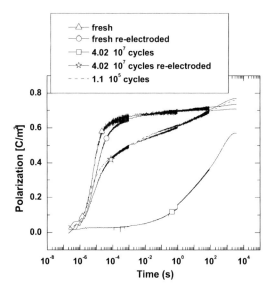

Figure 4.25: Switching data of fresh and fatigued $(4.02 \cdot 10^7$ cycles) samples before and after re-electroding. A fatigued sample of lower cycle number $(1.1 \cdot 10^5$ cycles) is shown for comparison.

4.2.3   Re-Electroding

Impedance Spectroscopy   After removal of the surface of fatigued samples by polishing the near electrode region (100μm on both sides), and re-application of electrodes, the additional, high frequency response disappears. This is clearly observed in the M* response of a fatigued sample before and after polishing (Figure 4.23). Data for a fresh sample is also shown for comparison. This clearly indicates that an interfacial layer is created under the electrodes during cycling. On removal of this interfacial layer by polishing (20μm on both sides), the polarization hysteresis loop was found to recover 90% of its initial height (Figure 4.24 b). Removal of only one sample surface yields only a partial recovery of the polarization indicating formation of an interfacial layer under each electrode, as expected from the bipolar pulse used during cycling.

Fast Switching   In order to complete the results obtained with impedance spectroscopy, it was interesting to observe the switching behavior of a fatigued sample which had been re-electroded. In order to obtain a reliable comparison with the fresh state, a fresh sample was also re-electroded. It can be observed in Figure 4.25 that re-electroding hardly changes the switching behavior of a fresh sample. Only a small shift of the switching curve to higher times is observed, indicating a slight increase of the time constant, probably due to a small change in the capacitance of the sample. The recovery observed for the polished (20μm on both sides) fatigued sample concerns both the slow and the fast switching components. Whereas the fatigued sample reaches only 5% of the polarization of a fresh sample after 1ms, it is recovered to 75% after re-electroding. For comparison, the switching curve of a sample fatigued to $1.1 \cdot 10^5$ cycles is plotted. It can be seen that it is nearly identical to the curve of the re-electroded sample. Thus, the switching behavior of the re-electroded sample is similar to a sample fatigued to a lower cycle number.

4.2.4   Thermal Annealing

The effects of thermal annealing on fatigue-induced changes were investigated using impedance spectroscopy and switching measurements.

Impedance Spectroscopy   Since it is well known that annealing at high temperature yields a recovery of the fatigue induced polarization loss, it is interesting to see the change of the fatigue-induced peak with thermal annealing. Figure 4.26 shows the change in M* response of a fatigued sample ($1.3 \cdot 10^7$ cycles) on annealing at 600 °C. The main semicircular arc associated with the bulk PZT response remains constant, however, the

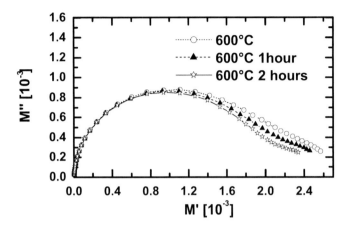

Figure 4.26: M* complex plane of a fatigued sample $(1.3 \cdot 10^7$ cycles) immediately after the temperature reached 600 °C , after 1 hour and 2 hours at 600 °C.

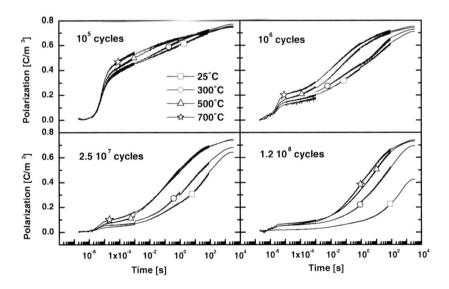

Figure 4.27: Polarization switching data for different annealing conditions and fatigue states.

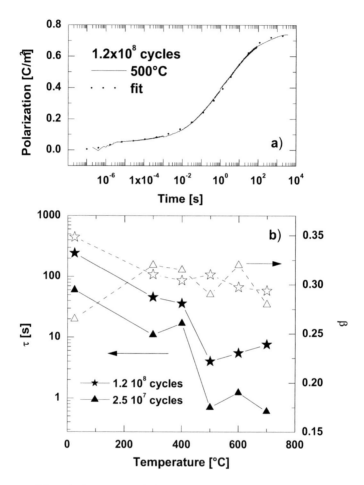

Figure 4.28: a) Stretched exponential fit for a particular measurement. b) Parameters obtained for two fits: relaxation time constant τ and exponent β.

additional semicircular arc at high frequencies clearly decreases in size with annealing time, indicating an increase of the associated capacitance.

Fast Switching   After fatigue, consecutive annealing steps from 300 °C to 700 °C in 100 °C steps were performed on each sample in order to avoid scattering effects from different samples. For the switching measurements described above, each sample was poled for the duration of 1 hour at 2kV/mm before measurement.

Figure 4.27 shows the polarization switching of samples in different fatigue states after cycling and consecutive annealing steps. For sake of clarity, not all of the annealing steps are displayed. As was previously observed (Figure 4.14), a fast component of the polarization P_{fast} switches faster than the extrinsic time constant of the electrical circuitry. The second component P_{slow} is highly retarded and exhibits a stretched exponential behavior. After different annealing steps, the recovery is only partial and the polarization switching remains strongly retarded. In contrast to the results after re-electroding, P_{fast} increases only slightly. Recovery of polarization is generally observed for the slowest components. For high cycle numbers, the curves shift to shorter times by several orders of magnitude after annealing, particularly at certain threshold temperatures. For $1 \cdot 10^5$, $2.5 \cdot 10^7$, and $1.2 \cdot 10^8$ cycles, a shift can be observed after annealing at 500 °C and for $1 \cdot 10^6$ cycles at 400 °C. For the highest cycle number ($1.2 \cdot 10^8$ cycles), the polarization does not reach saturation. After the first annealing step at 300 °C, a strong recovery is observed and saturation is almost reached within one hour. As previously, for all samples and annealing steps, the best fit of the time behavior was achieved using a Kohlrausch-Williams-Watts function (Figure 4.28 a): $P(t) = P_{fast} \exp\left(-t/\tau_{extr}\right) + P_{slow}[1 - \exp\left[-(t/\tau)^\beta\right]]$. The deviation of the fits at long periods of time (> 20 minutes) is due to the necessary but imperfect leakage current correction. Figure 4.28 b) depicts the development of the time constant τ and the relaxation exponent β with annealing temperature. The time constant decreases as expected from the shifts of the curves. β strongly changes after the first annealing step (increases for $2.5 \cdot 10^7$ and decreases for $1.2 \cdot 10^8$ cycles) and then settles at values around 0.3 .

4.2.5   Optical Observations and Reflectance Spectroscopy

Figure 4.29 shows the face of a fatigued sample in the immediate region underneath the electrodes. The color, uniformly yellow before cycling, changes after fatigue into brownish. However, this change is not uniform on the sample surface. The rim, left unelectroded at the edge of the sample, remains yellow, as well as a disc-shaped region in the center of the sample, corresponding to the position of the contact stamps during cycling. A dark spot

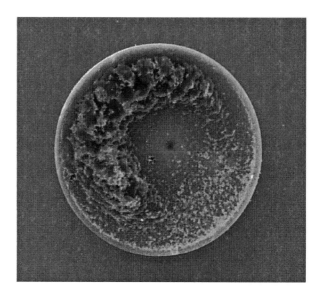

Figure 4.29: Picture of a fatigued sample after polishing away the electrode.

can be seen in the center of this region. In the surrounding area, some clouds, identified as microcracks, are observed and the color of the material is dark brown.

This color change motivated the optical measurements. Reflectance spectra were acquired for different samples in different fatigue states. Figure 4.30 a) displays the diffuse reflectance data of a fresh, a fatigued ($1.2 \cdot 10^8$ cycles) sample, and a fatigued sample which was annealed according to the steps described in Section 3.6. For comparison, the spectrum of an unfatigued sample with different doping (PZT 5H soft-doped from Morgan Matroc) is also shown. Figure 4.30 b) displays the corresponding K/S plot which was calculated using the Kubelka-Munk relation (see Section 3.5). If the strew coefficient remains constant, it displays the absorption of the sample. It can be observed that the fresh sample shows three fairly broad regions of low reflectance or strong absorption: in the range 375-475nm (3.3-2.6 eV), 725-850nm (1.5-1.75 eV) and a broad diffuse region around 1300nm (0.94eV). These absorption regions are also observed in the fatigued sample, but the absorption is additionally much stronger in between these regions. The fatigued sample shows a strong absorption over the whole frequency range from the near-infrared to the visible region with no sharp peaks. However, after thermal annealing, the material shows an almost complete recovery and the remission spectrum looks very similar to that of a fresh sample. The only difference in the spectrums is that the three absorption regions are slightly less accentuated in the annealed sample than in the fresh sample, whereas the sample has a stronger absorption in the near infrared between 1650 and 2500 nm. The PZT 5H sample, differently doped, shows a different spectrum. Only one absorption region is observed at 375 nm (3.3 eV).

Figure 4.31 a) displays the diffuse reflectance of a fresh, a unipolar cycled (10^8 cycles) and a mixed loaded sample and Figure 4.31 b) shows the corresponding K/S plot. The mixed loaded sample was cycled with synchronized electrical and mechanical loading. For further details on this fatigue mode, the reader is referred to [166]. The unipolar cycled sample exhibits the same absorption regions as the fresh sample. Compared to the fresh sample, the absorption is only slightly smaller in these regions and somewhat higher between them. The mixed loaded sample shows similar features but more pronounced. This sample especially has a higher absorption in the near infrared region when compared to the fresh sample.

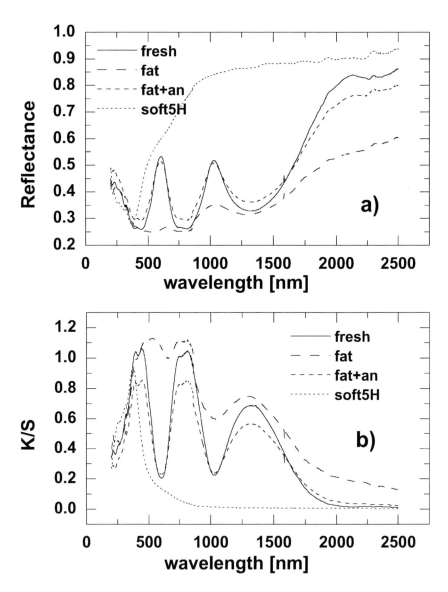

Figure 4.30: a) Reflectance and b) K/S spectrum of a fresh, fatigued, fatigued and annealed samples. The spectrum of a soft doped sample (Morgan Matroc 5H) is shown for comparison.

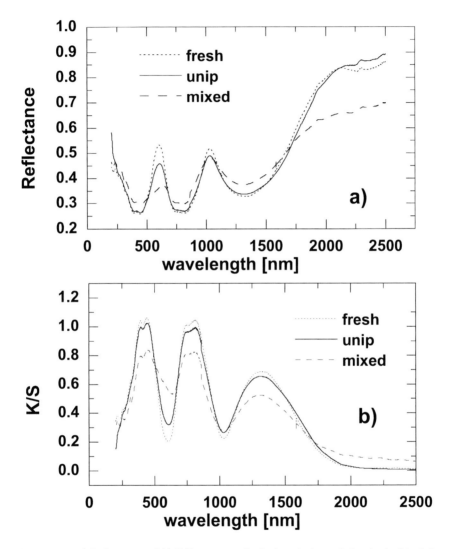

Figure 4.31: a) Reflectance and b) K/S spectrum of a fresh, unipolar cycled and mixed loaded samples

Chapter 5

Discussion

5.1 Unipolar Fatigue

The discussion of the effect of unipolar cycling is divided into 4 parts. First, the induced changes of the macroscopic parameters will be discussed, then the possible microscopic origin of these changes and finally a scenario for unipolar fatigue will be proposed.

5.1.1 Polarization and Strain Measurements

The results show a much lower fatigue in unipolar cycled than in bipolar cycled samples and agree with the measurements by Pan et al. [24]. The degradation of the polarization (ca. 5 % after 10^9 cycles) is found to be much smaller than that observed after bipolar fatigue where the polarization decrease reaches 70% after 10^8 cycles [17]. In a bipolar fatigued sample the total strain also strongly decreases with cycling, whereas it remains almost the same in a unipolar cycled sample. The increase and the spreading of the coercive field characteristic of bipolar fatigue is not observed in the unipolar case where the strain minima remain sharp and the slope of the polarization hysteresis at the coercive field is very steep. As mentioned in Section 2.3.3, the strong polarization decrease in the bipolar fatigue can be explained by the pinning of domains through agglomeration of point defects. The large distribution of the clamping energies of the domains induces a large distribution of the coercive fields and thereby diffuse minima in the strain hysteresis. Thus, unipolar cycling yields no strong pinning of the domains as in the bipolar fatigue and probably no agglomeration of point defects. It should be noticed that SEM observations (not shown here) after etching showed no change in the microstructure after unipolar cycling. This is different from the observations made in bipolar cycled samples, which showed the presence of corrosion paths [17]. Additionally, the sample color did not change as it is the case after bipolar fatigue. This indicates that the change in the microstructure induced by cycling is different in the unipolar and the bipolar case.

The only common feature of the unipolar cycling with the bipolar one is the asymmetry of the strain hysteresis. This asymmetry can be explained by the presence of an offset-field (shift of the polarization hysteresis loop along the voltage axis) or an offset-polarization (shift of the polarization hysteresis loop along the polarization axis) in the sample. An offset field has been reported in the literature as a consequence of ageing in thin films [137] and bulk ceramics [167] or as a consequence of unipolar cycling in thin films [28, 168]. However, in our measurements after bipolar and unipolar cycling, no significant shift of the polarization hysteresis loop along the field axis was observed. Thus in both cases, the asymmetry of the strain hysteresis can be explained by the formation of an offset polarization π in the bulk. According to the Landau-Devonshire theory, the strain of an

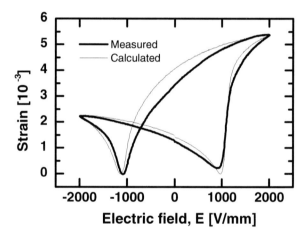

Figure 5.1: Strain hysteresis loop after $3.2 \cdot 10^8$ cycles. Measured strain, and calculated strain by squaring the measured polarization plus offset and rescaling.

electrostrictive material is proportional to the square of the total polarization (switchable and offset) [169]:

$$S(E) = Q(P(E) \pm \pi)^2. \tag{5.1}$$

where Q is the effective electrostrictive coefficient. The approximated asymmetric butterfly curve as depicted in Figure 5.1 is obtained for the parameters $Q=2.9 \cdot 10^2$ m^4/C^2, $\pi=0.074$ C/m^2. The degree of asymmetry depends on the value determined for π. However, it must be noticed that this fit, for several reasons, is only an approximation. First, whereas the polarization measurement takes into account the polarization of the whole sample, the strain hysteresis loop is measured at a particular location on the sample electrode, while the tip of the LVDT has a contact with the electrode, and the offset polarization is not expected to be uniform over the surface of the sample. So an average of the strain hysteresis loop over several locations would yield a better estimation of the asymmetry. Moreover, the behavior of the material is not a purely electrostrictive one because the S-P curve is not perfectly parabolic. The different contributions of 180° and 90° domain walls to strain and polarization hysteresis loops can explain the slight differences in coercive fields between both curves.

5.1.2 Offset Polarization

The question now is, what is the microscopic origin of this offset polarization. In the literature, a strain asymmetry was observed for a two layer geometry taken as a model for a multilayer stack actuators [170] and attributed to the formation of cracks on one side of the sample. The phenomenon of imprint, offset field, or polarization is well known and was many times reported in aging and fatigue experiments. Warren et al. [171] explained the offset polarization after thermal aging by the local alignment of defect dipoles in the sense of the model description by Robels and Arlt [172]. The mere alignment of defect dipoles along the polarization direction is believed to produce the polarization offset. The authors mention the implications of an offset polarization on strain but no published data are cited. Kholkin et al.[28] gave a direct measure of an offset polarization for PZT-thin films after bipolar fatigue by measuring the piezoelectric hysteresis. It was considered as the build-up of fixed internal polarization due to the pinning of ferroelectric domains in a preferred orientation. This was later correlated with observations showing fully clamped polarization using atomic force microscopy [83]. The authors discuss that the mere alignment of defect dipoles is not a sufficient mechanism to account for the offset polarization, because 10^{21} cm^{-3} dipoles would be needed to generate the effect. They furthermore observed that the offset polarization is induced under bipolar fatigue, while unipolar fatigue induces an offset-field.

In the experiments reported here, unipolar cycling yields both offsets but the effect of the offset polarization is more pronounced than the offset field. The application of a bipolar field after unipolar cycling (Figure 4.6) continuously removes this offset polarization. This is observed by the decrease of the asymmetry in the strain hysteresis accompanied by the continuous shift of the polarization hysteresis. Since the measurement set-up does not allow to measure the absolute value of the polarization, the offset along the polarization axis can only be observed because it is removed during a continuous measurement where the measurement capacitance is not short circuited. After applying 200 bipolar cycles, the strain asymmetry has been partially removed (Figure 4.6). The polarization hysteresis loop has been shifted by an amount of 0.019 C/m^2 and the total height of the loop has increased by 0.015 C/m^2, which is nearly the same amount. This means that the removed part of the offset-polarization has been regained for polarization switching. This argument supports the hypothesis of clamping of ferroelectric domains in a preferred direction, here the cycling direction, and that these clamped domains are responsible for the offset polarization and not a mere alignment of defect dipoles. A small amount of pinned domains and loss of polarization is sufficient to explain a fairly large asymmetry. Indeed, the fit in Figure 5.1 is made with a low value of π=0.074 C/m^2).

The continuous increase of the polarization and strain in Figure 4.5 for the fresh sample indicates the initial build-up of this imprint. After cycling there is no increase anymore, showing a stabilization of the process. But if the sample is cycled in the opposite direction, the offset is continuously removed. The removal is higher during the first cycles and reduces with increasing measurement cycles indicating a distribution in the clamping energy of the domains.

5.1.3   Nature of Pinning

There is little doubt that the offset described in these experiments is caused by freezing of some domains in cycling direction. The crucial question now is, what is the nature of the clamping. Several models have been proposed in the literature in order to explain imprint (in the field or polarization axis) in ferroelectric thin films or in bulk ceramics.

Arlt and coworkers [137, 173] explained the material changes in $BaTiO_3$ and PZT after ageing through the alignment of defect dipoles along the polarization direction. The underlying mechanism is based on the fact that there is an association between acceptor dopants on a Ti^{4+} site and oxygen vacancies. The pairs form defect dipoles in the unit cells. The acceptor ions are supposed to be immobile but the oxygen vacancies have a higher mobility and can diffuse in the oxygen octahedron, leading to an orientation of the defect-dipoles along the polarization direction under a DC load. By this reorientation, the force constant in particular for the $90°$ domain wall displacement is increased with time, and the domains become clamped, leading to the formation of an internal bias field and the polarization decrease. In this model, the alignment of defect dipoles yields the pinning of the domains. This model is supported by the fact that hard doping leads to a stronger imprint than soft doping. Very recently, Balke et al. [174] proposed an ageing model based on drift-diffusion of oxygen vacancies to the domain boundaries, in order to explain the domain clamping. They found the effect of oxygen vacancy drift to dominate over that of orientation of point-defect dipoles by up to three orders of magnitude.

In PLZT bulk ceramics, Warren and coworkers [95] showed that voltage offsets in the polarization hysteresis could be induced by illuminating the sample with band-gap light and applying a saturating bias field. The offset-voltage accompanied by a suppression of the switchable polarization were clearly identified to be due to electronic charge carriers. These electronic charge carriers were photoinduced and subsequently trapped at domain boundaries, yielding a pinning of the domains. In another set of experiments, Warren et al. [175] induced a thermal imprint in PZT thin films by heating the sample and applying a saturating bias field. The voltage shift was qualitatively similar but typically larger than the photoinduced one. This difference was attributed to oxygen vacancy motion, leading to significant alignment of defect dipoles similar to the model by Arlt.

Finally, another possibility, reported by Mihara et al. [168] was that the imprint may be due to rotation of new domains, which have large asymmetrical potential barriers along the direction of the applied electric field. This is the case for some $90°$ domains because of mechanical stresses. They argued that these domains would not switch under a single pulse but that a large number of unipolar pulses may cause the rotation of them, yielding an additional polarization.

The measurements of the hysteresis loops at high fields, after thermal annealing and the fast switching measurement give several indications about the stability and the nature of pinning. The high field experiment shows that the domain clamping can be recovered by applying high bipolar fields. In comparison to bipolar fatigue, the stability versus high fields is relatively high (Figure 4.8). Indeed, after the same treatment, in the same material after bipolar fatigue, Nuffer et al. [130] measured a complete recovery of the strain asymmetry. This is not the case here.

Thermal annealing shows that the clamping is very easily removed by increasing temperatures (Figure 4.9). After annealing at $200°$ C, the asymmetry has disappeared. This is different from the bipolar case. Nuffer et al. [130] showed that a fraction of the macroscopic asymmetry survived, even after annealing at fairly high temperatures ($600°C$). This indicates that different defects are responsible for domain pinning in the unipolar and bipolar case. Especially, if ionic defects were involved in the imprint yielded by unipolar cycling, they would not be expected to be removed at such low temperatures. Oxygen vacancies which are the most mobile ionic defects have a relatively high activation energy for motion of around 0.9-1 eV. Therefore, electronic charge carriers, which are not deeply trapped, are more likely involved, rather than ionic defects.

The switching experiment shows retardation in the time dependent polarization reversal after unipolar cycling. The switching is retarded but this delay is less pronounced than after bipolar fatigue and less stable. The sample had to be poled between each switching in order to cover a wide range of times. This led to a partial recovery at each switching, which explains the steps observed in Figure 4.10. Figure 4.11 shows an interesting feature. It can be observed that once the sample has switched, the polarization is completely free to switch, because the amount of reversed polarization during first switching (switch 1), switches as fast as in a fresh sample during second switching (switch 2). If the polarization is reversed until it reaches saturation, the sample is completely recovered. This indicates that the clamping is recovered by a single switching, which is different from bipolar fatigue. If ionic defects were responsible for the delay, a continuous recovery would be expected, because ions would drift on a very small scale after a single switching, whereas trapped electronic charge carriers can be excited in the conduction band and move over a long distance. If the delay was caused by the rotation of additional domains with asymmetrical potential barriers, the retardation should be observed during the second switching. Statistically, the sample should contain as many domains with an asymmetric potential along the field direction as opposite to it. Therefore, a delay should be observed in both directions of switching, which is not the case.

Thus, the results reported here support a trapping through electronic charge carriers rather than ionic species or rotation of domains with asymmetrical potential. However, a single trapped charge is probably not sufficient to clamp a domain. More likely, a charge accumulation at domain boundaries and grain boundaries with polarization discontinuity stabilizes the domain configuration and inhibits the screened domains from reorienting.

In contrast to bipolar fatigue, no color change is observed after unipolar cycling. The reflectance spectrum of a unipolar cycled sample shows no strong increase of the optical absorption in comparison to a fresh sample (Figure 4.31). It is surprising if trapped electronic charges are responsible for domain clamping. However, the trapped electronic charges are not necessarily the origin of optical absorption. Furthermore, trapped charges already existing in the fresh sample may only be redistributed, their concentration remaining constant. This would explain the small change in absorption.

After polishing the cycling electrodes and re-electroding the sample, the asymmetry in the measured strain hysteresis loop is not removed (Figure 4.12). This indicates that the domain clamping yielding the offset polarization is not limited to the near-electrode region but is a bulk effect.

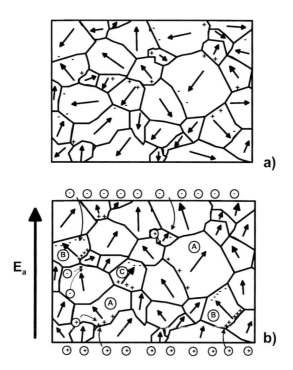

Figure 5.2: Schematic diagrams of a) an unpoled ceramic b) a poled ceramic after unipolar cycling where some grains are pinned by trapped charges.

5.1.4   Scenario of Unipolar Fatigue

The induced changes in the polarization and strain hysteresis loops after unipolar cycling can be qualitatively accounted for by considering the interaction between internal fields due to polarization charges and trapped charge carriers redistributed during cycling. Figure 5.2 a) depicts a schematic diagram of an unpoled polycrystalline ceramic. For the sake of simplicity, each grain is considered to be constituted of a monodomain. The arrows indicate only the direction of the polarization in the grains but not their value. The average of the macroscopic polarization is 0. Some trapped defect charges are distributed at polarization discontinuities.

Figure 5.2 b) shows the possible mechanisms occurring during cycling. When the unipolar cycling field is applied, the domains are reoriented in the direction of the applied field. During cycling, trapped electronic charge carriers are liberated and new charge carriers are generated. They migrate and are trapped at polarization discontinuities, where they compensate the polarization charges. Polarization discontinuities occur either at charged domain walls ([176]) or most likely at grain boundaries which represent ideal locations for defect trapping, due to the breaking in the crystal periodicity. Accumulating charge carriers at the domain discontinuities screen internal depolarizing fields ([6]) and stabilize the domain configuration. There is a distribution in the stabilization of the domains depending on the concentration of the trapped charges. Three types of domains can be distinguished if an AC field is applied. Most of domains (A) remain free to switch. The switching of domains C is partially hindered by some trapped charges and the domains C will switch at higher fields, yielding the increase of the coercive field observed in the first switching in Figure 4.7. Domains B are stabilized by a higher concentration of trapped charge carriers and will be pinned and not switch. These clamped domains yield the small polarization loss, and because they are pinned in the cycling direction, they are responsible for the offset polarization, which induces the asymmetry of the strain hysteresis loop. As noticed before, only a small amount of pinned polarization is necessary to yield a significant offset in the strain hysteresis loop (Figure 5.1). The clamping is removed if a sufficient field is applied during long enough time in the opposite direction to cycling. The trapped charge carriers are then liberated and redistributed.

The question now is, what is the driving force responsible for the liberation of electronic charge carriers during cycling. Dimos et al. [177] and Grossman et al. [178] proposed models for imprint in PZT thin films. Their explanation is based on the existence of a thin layer at the interface between electrode and ferroelectric, in which the spontaneous polarization is absent. It is believed that this layer is either a space charge layer or a chemically or mechanically distorted layer, which does not take part in the polarization reversal process [178]. This so called dead-layer separates the external screening charges in the electrodes and polarization charges, leading to an incomplete screening of the depolarizing field and thus to a residual depolarizing field. In the model by Dimos et al. [177], the driving force for charge separation is the residual depolarizing field, whereas in the model by Grossman et al., the driving force is the field arising in the interior of the dead layer. These models seem to be reasonable in thin films because of the dominant role of the electrodes. In bulk ferroelectrics, the electrodes are not expected to have such an influence, and the measurements demonstrated that the offset-polarization is rather a bulk effect, thus a dominant effect of a dead layer at the electrode-ferroelectric interface does not seem to be realistic. However, a thin layer equivalent to a dead-layer may exist at grain boundaries and a similar scenario may occur in each grain. Another possibility, which is to my opinion more likely in bulk PZT, is that the driving force for charge separation may originate from the fact that some domains switch back during cycling.

In each cycle, when the field reaches zero, most of the domains remain oriented along the applied field and only undergo a small change in polarization, which is not high enough to liberate trapped charge carriers, but some $90°$ domains switch back because of mechanical clamping. Switching induces a change in the orientation of the polarization thus a change of the depolarizing field, which can provide the driving force necessary to separate electronic charge carriers or detrap some electronic charges. Finally, an additional contribution can come from charge injection from the electrodes through a Schottky-effect as illustrated in Figure 5.2 b).

5.2 Bipolar Fatigue

The discussion of the bipolar fatigue phenomenon is divided into four parts. First, the identified microstructural changes in the material after fatigue will be interpreted. Second, the evolution of the switching behavior of the material will be discussed on the basis of these changes. The following section deals with the thermal stability of these modifications. A last part will discuss the possible scenarios responsible for bipolar fatigue on the basis of the results obtained.

5.2.1 Microstructural Changes

The measurements of impedance spectroscopy, reflectance spectroscopy and polishing the near electrode-region deliver information on the changes induced by bipolar cycling in the microstructure of PZT.

Impedance Spectroscopy

Dielectric relaxations in ferroelectric ceramics occur at various frequencies, depending on the type of chemical or physical defects. Space charge relaxations ($\sim 10^2$-10^6 Hz) are related to conductivity phenomena. Domain wall relaxations ($\sim 10^2$-10^6 Hz) are closely related to defects. High frequency relaxations ($\sim 10^7$-10^{10} Hz) are either ascribed to piezo-electric resonance of domains, or to the so-called correlation chain model [179].

The most important features observed in this study were obtained at temperatures well above the Curie-temperature, in the paraelectric phase. Thus, there is no contribution of ferroelectric domains in the measured responses. Through heating of the sample, relaxation processes occurring at low frequencies could be shifted into the frequency range of the spectrometer. As mentioned above in Section 3.4, each response or peak corresponds to a relaxation process related to a conductivity phenomenon occurring in a certain electroactive region. In order to extract resistance and capacitance values of each region within a sample from impedance spectroscopy data, it is necessary to have an equivalent circuit to model the electrical response. The capacitance and resistance values were extracted here from each peak by modelling this peak with a parallel resistor-capacitor element. In ferroelectric ceramics such as $BaTiO_3$ [180], in most cases, the different responses can be modelled by parallel RC elements connected in series.

The results show that a fresh sample exhibits a single peak, located at the same frequency in the Z and M formalisms for a given temperature. This peak is associated with the bulk of the sample. Fatigued samples show an extra peak in the M" plots, which is not obvious in the Z" plots. This demonstrates the usefulness of a combined usage of impedance and modulus spectroscopy, as was suggested by Sinclair and West [163]. The advantage of this technique is that the M" and Z" peaks for a particular RC combination should be coincident on the frequency scale (ideal Debye case). Hence, the power of combined formalisms is that the Z" plot highlights phenomena with largest resistance, whereas the M" plot picks out those with smallest capacitances (see Section 3.4). This second response indicates the presence, in fatigued samples at high temperatures, of an electroactive region of higher capacitance and lower resistivity than the bulk.

This response vanished completely after polishing off the near-electrode region, indicating that it is associated with the volume located underneath the electrodes. The polishing was accompanied by a high recovery of the polarization hysteresis loop (Figure 4.24) and of the time dependent polarization reversal (Figure 4.25). This shows that the near electrode region is directly correlated with the loss in polarization induced by fatigue and contributes to a great part of it. In addition, this region yields a parasitic capacitance in series with the bulk, and thus can explain the decrease of the effective permittivity of a fatigued sample in comparison to a fresh sample (Figure 4.19). The capacitance of this layer decreased with cycle number. This can be explained, either by a decrease in dielectric constant, or more likely, by an increase in thickness of the fatigue induced layer. The increase of the fatigue induced response with cycle number, thus the layer thickness, shows a good correlation with the decrease of the polarization, except for the highest cycle number (Figure 4.22).

In the material investigated here, the nature of the interfacial region remains unclear. Microcracks, which are observed underneath the electrodes, could be at the origin of a parasitic capacitance and yield a voltage drop through this layer, and then, a lower fraction of the applied voltage seen by the bulk [126]. However, the capacitance extracted from the fatigue induced peak exhibits a Curie-Weiss behavior with temperature, which would not be expected if we believe in the hypothesis of microcracks. The fact that microcracks are not directly responsible for polarization loss is further supported by the annealing experiments (see Section 5.2.3). The growth of a non-ferroelectric layer (also called passive layer or blocking layer) is a possible reason for polarization loss (see Section 2.3.3). Larsen et al. [145] interpreted the thickness dependence of the reciprocal capacitance of PZT thin films, the coercive voltage, and the polarization measured by pulse switching, by the existence of a non-ferroelectric layer at the electrode-ferroelectric interface. They explained the polarization loss by a voltage drop through this layer. The Curie-Weiss behavior exhibited here by the fatigue induced response indicates that the layer is more likely constituted of a disturbed ferroelectric material,e. g. due to an increasing amount of defects. These results correlate well with the results of Lee et al. [147]. They reported the existence of an interfacial capacitance in Pt/PZT/Pt thin films after fatigue, which they determined from the thickness dependence of low field effective dielectric permittivity. The capacitance of this interfacial layer decreased with increasing fatigue, while the dielectric permittivity of the bulk PZT film remained constant. They assigned the formation of this interfacial layer to the pile-up of oxygen vacancies at the Pt/PZT interface, which they made responsible for fatigue. In a further work [181], they attributed the high fatigue resistance of $SrBi_2Ta_2O_9$ (SBT) and $SrBi_2Nb_2O_9$ (SBN) ceramics as compared to PZT, to their high conductivity. Specifically, they found an activation energy for the conduction processes of around 0.9 eV, which was attributed to the motion of oxygen vacancies. They argued that the fatigue resistance of SBN and SBT was due to the easy recovery of oxygen vacancies from traps, avoiding their pile-up.

The activation energy of the bulk response corresponds to half of the band gap of PZT which means that the conduction is dominated by excitation of intrinsic charge carriers. The activation energies associated with the fatigue induced response are here in the range 0.35-0.65 eV and do not correspond to a conduction mechanism dominated by oxygen vacancies motion. However, this does not exclude the presence of oxygen vacancies. Bharadwja and Krupanidhi [182] for example, found an activation energy of the space charge limited conduction in $PbZrO_3$ of 0.56 eV, which they attributed to shallow traps. They evoked the possibility that these shallow traps were induced by the presence of oxygen vacancies which act as dopants. Also the presence of oxygen vacancies could explain the high conductivity in the interface layer compared to the bulk. But the range of activation energies found in the present work is large and further investigations are necessary to determine the conduction mechanism.

The formation and the growing of the interfacial layer observed here can lead to a polarization loss through clamping of the domains by defects, or as mentioned above, through a smaller fraction of the applied voltage seen by the bulk. These two possibilities will be examined in more detail in the next section (see Section 5.2.2).

Optical Observations and Reflectance Spectroscopy

The simple observation of a fatigued sample in the immediate region underneath the electrode shows some interesting features. The color change is inhomogeneous over the sample surface and shows that the fatigue is probably not homogeneous. The yellow area corresponding to the position of the stamps seems to indicate that the material is less fatigued at this location. This may be due to the mechanical clamping exerted by the stamps on this area, which modifies the switching properties in this region and thus the fatigue resistance. The dark regions, which correspond to the regions where the sample is more fatigued, show also a lot of microcracks. This indicates that microcracks are involved in the fatigue process.

In a previous work, etch grooves were rendered visible in strongly etched surfaces by scanning electron microscopy after fatigue [126]. These structures were identified as defect agglomerates responsible for domain pinning. It is clear now, that they cannot be made responsible for most part of polarization loss in this composition, because they were located predominantly in the center of the sample. But, even in the bulk, fatigue induces a change in the defect chemistry.

The reflectance spectroscopy results confirm that there is a change in the electronic structure after fatigue. In the acquired spectra, the region below 375 nm (>3.3eV) is unclear because it corresponds to the edge of the conduction band, therefore an intense absorption should be observed because of excitation of electrons from the valence band into the conduction band. However there is an increase in reflectance. This may be due to a re-emission through luminescence. Vibrational processes can be excluded for the interpretation of these data, because they would yield sharp features in the near-infrared region, which is not observed [165]. The three absorption regions in the sample are probably related to the doping of the composition PIC 151 because the Morgan Matroc 5H (soft but unknown dopants) composition does not show these absorptions. The doping species create local energy levels or narrow bands in the band-gap. Due to the great number of potential defects, which give rise to local energy levels or defect bands in the band gap [183], the data do not allow to clearly assign this absorption peaks to particular electronic processes. The fatigued sample shows a broad absorption over the whole frequency range of the spectrum, in the infrared and visible regions. Such a broad spectral absorption could suggest that there is a broad distribution of occupied states in the band gap, but more likely it is due to an increasing number of charge carriers, which occupy states close to the band edges. The conduction and valence bands may not have sharp edges but tails of states extending from the top of the valence band and the bottom of the conduction band into the forbidden gap [183]. Fatigue may lead to an occupation of these shallow traps by charge carriers. Under illumination, these charge carriers, electrons or holes, can be excited into the conduction or valence band with a broad range of energies leading to a broad absorption. After annealing, this absorption has disappeared indicating that these shallow traps have been emptied.

Thus, these results show that changes in the defect structure occur in the whole sample after fatigue, in the near electrode region and in the bulk. However, these spectra were acquired in the bulk of the sample and not in the immediate region underneath the electrodes. Thus, the electronic defect charges responsible for the increasing absorption are not the dominant cause of fatigue because the polarization loss is in large extent related to the near electrode regions. However, they may contribute to a smaller extent to the delay observed in switching. Further investigations are necessary, in order to more consistently understand the optical processes occurring in the material.

New Results

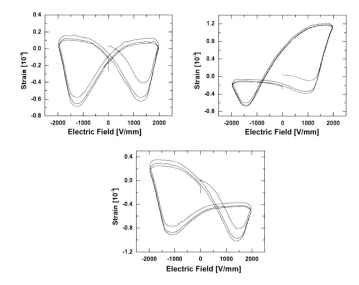

Figure 5.3: Strain hysteresis loops measured on three different locations on the sample after bipolar cycling ($1.8 \cdot 10^6$ cycles).

New results, obtained very recently in our group, are worth to be mentioned in the framework of this discussion because they bring insights into some aspects of fatigue in bulk PZT [184]. Figure 5.3 shows strain hysteresis loops acquired at three different locations on the sample surface with a slightly different set-up than that described in Section 3.3.1. The sample was not set on a plane surface but between two fine tips in order to achieve a local measurement of strain. It can be seen that the degradation of the strain hysteresis loops is different at the three locations and that they exhibit asymmetries in opposite directions or no asymmetry at all. This confirms the fact that fatigue is inhomogeneous on the sample surface. The different asymmetries indicate that in a column situated between the two tips there is a preferred orientation in the pinning of the domains, yielding an offset polarization in one direction or the other.

A second interesting result concerns a 2% La doped PZT, a different doping than the material investigated in this work. For this composition, polishing off the near electrode region after fatigue yielded almost no recovery of the polarization hysteresis loop. This indicates, that, depending on the composition, fatigue can be related to defects located very close to the electrodes or in the bulk. This also suggests that different mechanisms and defects can be responsible for fatigue.

5.2.2   Fast Switching Measurements

The switching measurement gives interesting information on the nature of pinning after bipolar fatigue. So far, the domain pinning has been considered in the literature as a static clamping in the literature. Under constant field, clamped domains were considered to be completely frozen, unable to switch. The measurements presented here first show that this is not the case, because after a long time, all the samples reach saturation, except the sample with the highest cycle number. They also show the relevance of this method, compared to the measurement of a hysteresis loop with a triangular field at a single frequency. This method allows to observe different frequencies and to resolve the delay of switching in the time domain.

Several functions have been tested to fit the time dependent polarization reversal. The best fit was obtained by a Kohlrausch-Williams-Watts (KWW) function (Equation 4.1). The KWW function can be be considered as arising from a superposition of exponentials:

$$e^{-(t/\tau_{KWW})^{\beta_{KWW}}} = \int_0^\infty e^{-t/\tau} \cdot \rho_{KWW}(\tau) d\tau \qquad (5.2)$$

which defines the KWW distribution function $\rho_{KWW}(\tau)$. To derive $\rho_{KWW}(\tau)$, Equation 5.2 has to be rewritten in the form of a Laplace-integral, and the inverse Laplace transform can be calculated using a series form [185]. The obtained distribution function was numerically computed, using the software Mathcad®, for the parameters τ and β obtained from the

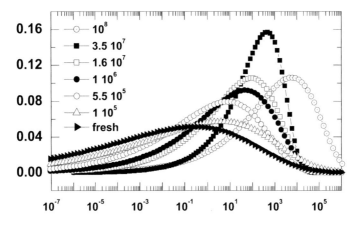

Figure 5.4: Distribution of time constants depending on the fatigue state

fits of the curves in Figure 4.14. The KWW distribution function for the different cycle numbers are displayed in Figure 5.4 as $\tau \cdot \rho_{\mathrm{KWW}}(\tau)$, the form traditionally used to present such distribution functions. With increasing fatigue, the time constants increase and the increasing β values yield a more narrow distribution of the time constants (except for the highest cycle number).

The polarization reversal in ferroelectric materials has not been fully understood so far and is still subject to discussion. The switching in single crystals and most thin films is well described on the basis of the extended Kolmogorov-Avrami (K-A) phase transition theory, further developed by Ishibashi and Takagi [186]. In the hypothesis of a deterministic nucleation, the reversed polarization under external DC field is expressed as:

$$\Delta P = P_s[exp(\frac{-t}{\tau})^d] \qquad (5.3)$$

where τ is the time constant for switching, d the dimensionality of domain growth and P_s the saturation polarization [187]. Thus, d should be at least equal to one. However, exponent factors (β in Figure 4.18) ranging between 0.1 and 0.3 were found here. The broadness of the distribution of time constants is, in the material investigated here, much more important than the K-A theory predicts. Therefore, this theory does not seem to well explain the extremely long stretch in switching observed here. It is now interesting to examine which microscopic mechanisms are likely to yield such an extended distribution of time constants and why this distribution changes during fatigue.

The Non-Fatigued Case   Many microscopic mechanisms are recognized to yield a stretched exponential behavior, that is for values of the exponent β comprised in the interval [0,1] [188]. For the non-fatigued sample, 25% of the polarization switching is delayed. The distribution of time constants of this fraction can be explained by a distribution of locally acting fields. It has long been established that the relaxation time τ exponentially depends on the applied electric field, $\tau \propto exp(E_a/E_{applied})$, where E_a is known as the activation field [5]. In suitably oriented single crystals the local field is identical to the external field unless internal screening fields are present. Switching occurs, once a domain seed exceeds a critical size. In a polycrystalline material, the local projections of the external field onto the permitted polarization directions in each grain cover a wide range of local fields and thus time constants. As lead zirconate titanate close to the morphotropic phase boundary permits fourteen variants for polarization, the orientation distribution effect is not as important as it would be e.g. for $BaTiO_3$, where only 6 variants are permitted by symmetry. The field distribution should therefore only provide a very small retardation. A certain contribution of point defects present in the material can also be responsible for the initial 25% of slow component and has been discussed in previous studies as the underlying cause of the strong delay in switching [189].

Fatigue   The experimental results show that cyclic loading induces a continuous increase of the average time constant and an increase of the stretching exponent β. Four possible aspects explaining these changes will be discussed, a voltage drop through the near-electrode region, random fields, clustering of point defects, and cascaded switching throughout the microstructure. Each of these aspects contributes to the retardation of the switching and to the broadening of the distribution of time constants at different locations of the sample.

The angular distribution of grains cannot be responsible for the changes in time constant observed due to cyclic loading, because it simply does not change.

As was shown by Lohse et al. [190] in PZT thin films, the application of switching fields only slightly higher than the coercive field yields a retardation of the switching over several orders of magnitude in time, which cannot be explained by the classical theory of switching. Thus, a voltage drop through the interface layer described in Section 5.2.1 and a lower field seen by the bulk may play a relevant role in the retardation of switching behavior after fatigue. The voltage drop can be estimated by modelling a fatigued sample as a series of three ideal capacitances (Figure 5.5): a capacitor representing the bulk material (C_b), and two representing dielectric interface layers in the near electrode region

(C_i). The capacitance value in the fatigued sample can be roughly formulated as follows:

$$\frac{1}{C_m} = \frac{1}{C_b} + \frac{2}{C_i} \tag{5.4}$$

where C_m is the measured capacitance, where the complications evoked by Brakovsky [146] concerning a linear capacitance series for a ferroelectric will be neglected. The thickness of the interface layer is assumed to be negligible in comparison to the bulk thickness. The bulk is assumed to be composed of nearly unfatigued material so its capacitance is nearly equal to the capacitance of a fresh sample, which is derived from the impedance data. For a sample cycled with $3\cdot10^7$ cycles, $C_m = 0.55$ nF and $C_b \approx C_{fresh} = 1.8$ nF. This gives a parasitic capacitance $C_i/2 = 0.79$ nF in the fatigued sample. If a voltage of $V_a = 2000$ V is applied to the sample, we find $2V_i = 1400$ V and $V_b = 600$ V. A voltage of 600 V applied to a fresh sample was found to be insufficient to switch the sample. After one hour, less than 20% of the total switchable polarization are switched (not shown here) whereas a voltage of 2000 V applied to a fatigued sample yielded an almost complete switching (Figure 4.14). This shows that the switching behavior of fatigued samples cannot be explained by a simple voltage drop through a non-ferroelectric interface layer. This is another indication which supports the fact that the interface layer must be ferroelectric. This layer has to switch, so that the local field becomes high enough to induce the switching of the bulk. However, this simple model gives only a rough estimation of the voltage drop, because it considers that the interface layer acts as a perfect capacitance. This is not the case because the interface layer was shown to be more conductive than the bulk so the total impedance of the layer should be considered and it cannot be excluded that charges build up at the interface between this layer and the bulk because of a leakage in the layer, and lead to an increase of the field seen by the bulk.

The switching in the sample as a whole most likely is dependent on the switching in the near electrode region. The delay of switching and the very broad distribution of time constants in this region may be the result of several mechanisms.

In relaxor ferroelectrics, it is well known that the strong retardation is caused by inherently existent random fields [191, 192]. As was shown initially by Imry and Ma [193], random fields within a mono-domain crystal will cause this domain to break down into smaller entities irrespective of the type of field and corresponding order parameter, if a coupling between the random fields and the order parameter exists. The order parameter in our case is the polarization, and a coupling to charged defects is evident. The transition occurs instantaneously in two dimensions and necessitates a threshold in three dimensions. Thus, a certain minimum concentration of charged defects must be present in order to induce a change of the domain system due to random fields in three dimensions. While the origin of the random fields is not as evident in relaxor ferroelectrics, isolated

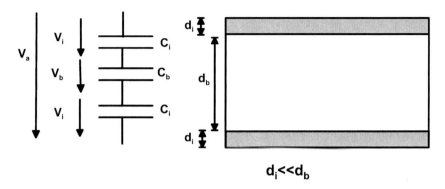

Figure 5.5: Modelling of a fatigued sample through capacitances in series considering two interfacial layers.

magnetic impurities are the classic origin of random fields in magnetic systems [194]. In the case of ferroelectrics, random fields could originate from charged impurities at random locations. This was already discussed in the original theoretical results by Imry and Ma [193] and recently correlated to experimental data in PZT [189]. If the number of charge carriers inducing random fields exceeds the above-mentioned threshold, a mono-domain ferroelectric will break down into smaller domains (Figure 5.6 a). A change of the domain pattern as a result of cyclic fatigue loading has indeed been observed in this material. It was, however, interpreted as the result of the formation of point defect agglomerates [84]. The formation of random fields is a possible explanation for the breakdown of the domain system into smaller units. Impurity ions initially neutralized by the corresponding number of electrons or holes are ionized. Experimental proof for this is derived from electron paramagnetic resonance measurements (different PZT dopants than in the present study), [22] where a change of valency of acceptor dopants Fe^{3+} and Pt^{3+} due to cyclic loading was demonstrated. Furthermore, the reflectance spectroscopy results show that a large number of optically excitable electronic charge carriers are induced by fatigue, as can be seen in the reflectance spectroscopy results. Simultaneously, liberated electronic charge carriers become mobile and contribute to the higher conductivity observed in the near electrode layer. Some of the ionized impurity ions or highly localized electronic defects remain localized (Figure 5.6 b) and generate an increased number of random local fields within the grains or potentially at their perimeter, possibly the grain boundary. However, the increasing number of random centers leads to an increase of the stretching exponent, so this effect must be accompanied by an effect which yields a decrease in randomness.

A further aspect of the fatigue mechanism comes into play due to point defect ag-

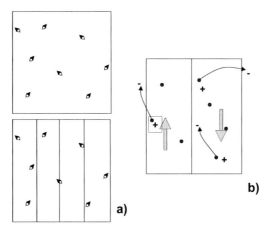

Figure 5.6: a) Schematic explanation of random fields and breaking of the monodomain into a polydomain structure. b) Ionization of new defects during cycling.

glomeration [144, 84, 17]. In the first case, the distribution of point defects changes the character of the domain system itself, but essentially maintains its mobility range, which is usually a grain. The clustering of point defects, additionally, changes the mobility range of the domain system as a whole to smaller grain segments. High barriers to domain wall motion are formed by these clusters, because stable domain states are induced in their immediate proximity [84]. The remaining switchable domain system now has to overcome these clusters in order to switch completely. As the number and size of the agglomerates increase with cycling, more and more grains become affected, yielding an increase of the time constant τ. The stretching exponent β increases after a certain number of fatigue cycles. This change describes a lower degree of randomness (increase of β), which can be explained by the fact that the point defects are less randomly distributed.

The modified local switching times can have an influence on global switching on a larger scale, through the polycrystalline material. Switching in general occurs at applied field values which are far below the thermodynamic coercive field. In a uniaxial single crystal, switching is initiated at domain seeds and the domains propagate as far as possible through homogenous regions of the crystal towards the opposite electrode with limited sideways growth [195]. The local field is strong enough to form instantaneously sufficient domain wall area for seed inhibition only at some defect or inhomogeneity. The enhanced local fields are therefore crucial for the switching process itself. According to Arlt and Calderwood [196], for grains in polycrystals, the vicinity of the next neighbor plays a similar role in enhancing the local electric field above the switching threshold. Once the nearest neighbor has switched, the switching probability of this particular grain is strongly enhanced due to the increased polarization mismatch at the grain boundary, irrespective of the above-mentioned grain misorientations (Figure 5.7 a). Direct communication between neighboring grains and domains is nearly instantaneous in a non-fatigued ferroelectric, and relaxation can occur at such a high speed that it is not accessible to experimental measurements. However, it may be hindered in fatigued material, e.g. through trapping of charged defects at grain boundaries. This conditional or cascaded switching is another general source of stretched exponential relaxation [197] and in particular increases the time constants involved. The degree of randomness, on the other hand, cannot increase, because this would lead to another decrease of β (total randomness is equivalent to $\beta \rightarrow 0$), which is not observed. A recent microstructural finite element study revealed that such switching propagation fronts do arise for ferroelastic coupling [198] and the arguments by Arlt and Calderwood [196] also support this pattern for ferroelectrics. In the present material, the fatigue-induced changes located underneath the electrodes delay the switching of the whole sample. This shows that switching probably occurs first in the grains in contact with the electrode and, according to Figure 5.7 a) propagates nearly perpendicular to it in the direction of the opposite electrode. Since fatigue is inhomogeneous over the sample surface, each switching "column" would have different time constants yielding a distribution of time constants over the sample.

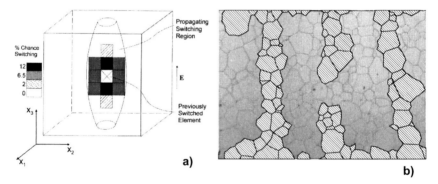

Figure 5.7: a) Picture of the local field in a spherical inclusion from [199]. b) Schematic explanation of cascaded switching.

Several other more elaborate microscopic descriptions of stretched exponential behavior may be devised [200, 201] and have been discussed for microscopically better-defined systems such as glass or various magnetic systems. Further detailed discussions of the fatigue effect in PZT can only follow after more complementary experiments, e.g. on the changes of the electronic state of point defects, have been undertaken.

In summary, bipolar cycling was shown, for the composition investigated here, to retard strongly domain switching. The defects located in the near electrode region have a predominant effect in the switching delay of the whole sample. Random fields of ionized defects within the bulk grains are likely to be the initial contribution to stretched exponential polarization switching. A subsequent contribution to retardation is provided by the clustering of point defects to extended agglomerates within each grain. As a result, the domain mobility range is reduced and/or filled with intermediate size obstacles hampering the domain dynamics locally. On a larger scale, cascaded switching throughout a polycrystalline microstructure constitutes an overall mechanism of switching retardation.

5.2.3 Thermal Annealing

The experimental results indicate that thermal annealing yields a different recovery than re-electroding. Since the damages responsible for polarization loss lie for the most part in a nearby electrode region, the measurement provides information about the thermal stability of this layer. Figure 4.26 clearly shows that the response induced by this layer is reduced after thermal annealing indicating a decrease of the layer thickness or an increase of its dielectric constant or both. This reduction correlates well with the regain in polarization.

So far, fatigue recovery after annealing [131, 48, 130] has been identified by measuring polarization hysteresis loops at single distinct frequencies and recovery is high at e.g. 0.02 Hz [130]. From the present study, it is clear that recovery from fatigue by annealing is incomplete. The induced damages persistently suppress fast switching.

The crucial question now is which microscopic defects can be annealed in the temperature range covered here. Microcracks should not heal at 700 °C. The fact that the most cycled sample ($1.2 \cdot 10^8$ cycles) reaches saturation within one hour after the first annealing step (300 °C) shows that microcracking is not a significant retardation mechanism for switching and at maximum suppresses 5% of polarization switching overall (Figure 4.27).

The observed discontinuous annealing steps at certain temperatures support the fact that several mechanisms are involved in fatigue and recover at different temperatures because of different activation energies for their recovery. Three dominant microscopic mechanisms were previously discussed for switching retardation (Section 5.2.2) (a) random fields, [191] (b) point defect agglomeration, [11] and (c) cascaded switching across the microstructure on the grain level. Mechanism (a) is known to dominate switching in disordered systems. Mechanism (b) obviously interferes with domain switching for growing defect sizes. Mechanism (c) essentially extends the retardation found on the individual grain level to macroscopically longer times. The reason for mechanism (c) is that electric fields at a certain grain are lower than the local threshold, unless the neighboring grains have already switched.

The occurrence of mechanism (a) is experimentally supported by a color change of the samples during fatigue which is recovered by annealing. This is verified by the recovery of electronic band gap states due to annealing observed by reflectance spectroscopy. Impurity ions, host ions, or oxygen vacancies [202] initially neutralized by the corresponding number of electrons or holes are ionized during cyclic loading explaining the darkening of the sample and constitute the above-mentioned retardation mechanism. During annealing these electronic states are excited into the conduction or valence band and recombine. The domain mobility re-increases.

Oxygen vacancies have been assigned to constitute the dominant point defects responsible for mechanism (b), because they are the most mobile ionic defects [11, 143]. The resulting agglomerates become high barriers to domain wall motion. In the present study the polarization remains strongly degraded even after annealing at $700\,^{\circ}C$, which indicates that some contribution to fatigue is thermally very stable. A thermodynamic stable superstructure of planar oxygen vacancy clusters in the perovskite structure has been reported in the literature when the concentration of vacancies exceeds a certain threshold [140]. This could explain why clusters are still present after annealing. They are thermodynamically stable but point defects do not have enough time to order during cooling from the sintering temperature. Only the bipolar cycling generates sufficient driving forces at lower temperatures to reorder these defects locally into their thermodynamically stable locations.

Mechanism (c) may be induced during fatigue by a change in the defect chemistry at grain boundaries. Charged defects may segregate at grain boundaries building space charge layers, which may screen the field exerted by one grain onto its neighbor. The driving force on switching of neighboring grains by the polarization mismatch at the grain boundary is now reduced and switching is further retarded. Thermal annealing may yield a redistribution of these defects and improve the interaction of domain systems between neighboring grains.

Recovery from fatigue due to thermal annealing is thus only partial. Electronic defects are most likely to recombine at low annealing temperatures, while clusters of ionic species, most likely oxygen vacancies, constitute thermally stable entities.

5.2.4   Scenarios of Bipolar Fatigue

The effects of fatigue induced microstructural changes on the macroscopic parameters, especially the time dependent polarization reversal, were discussed in the previous sections. The question now is, how these changes are brought about during cycling, what are the driving forces inducing the defects responsible for fatigue, and why these defects are mostly located underneath the electrodes in the material investigated here. On the basis of the obtained results, we may briefly discuss the relevance of the different models proposed in the literature (see Section 2.3.3) and suggest possible explanations for fatigue in this particular PZT composition.

Mechanics models explain the polarization loss directly by a voltage drop at microcracks leading to an insufficient field seen by the ferroelectric in order to switch. Such a scenario is unlikely in our composition. The recovery observed after thermal annealing showed that this effect does not play a dominant role. The microcracks may be a consequence of the fatigue phenomenon because of increasing mechanical stresses, or they may play an indirect role in fatigue. A lot of microcracks were observed underneath the electrodes. The presence of microcracks induces high polarization discontinuities at their faces. Thus, there must be a high number of charge carriers trapped there, in order to compensate the polarization. When the domains move, if they are deeply trapped, they may hinder the movement of the domain system. If they are not deeply trapped, they may move on the crack faces or be liberated and trapped further in the bulk where they may contribute to fatigue.

An interfacial layer located in the near electrode region was shown here to be induced by cycling. But it was also shown, in the hypothesis that this layer would not be ferroelectric, that the voltage drop would be too high so that the sample can switch. The impedance spectroscopy data suggest that this layer is ferroelectric. Thus the model of the passive layer is not believed to play a dominant role on the scale of the whole sample. However, on a local scale, a possible scenario could be that a thin "dead layer" is induced at grain boundaries during cycling due to segregation of defects. This would hinder the communication between the grains and retard the polarization reversal through cascaded switching.

The model of seed inhibition proposed by Tagantsev [119] may occur in thin films but is unlikely in bulk ceramics. This model implies the formation of a monodomain in each grain after complete switching. This is not the case here, since numerous domain walls are observed in each grain when the sample is poled [11]. The switching in polycrystals is dominated by domain wall movement because the complexity of the microstructure does not allow to remove the domain walls from the individual grains entirely. Therefore a mechanism of domain wall pinning, that is a clamping of the domains because of their interaction with defects, is the most reasonable scenario. An important point shown by this work is that the pinning of domains must be seen in the light of retardation of domain kinetics and not as a static clamping.

The nature of the defects inducing this retardation is still unclear. The changes in the permittivity and conductivity in the near electrode region after fatigue are probably due to a change in the concentration of defects in this region. Thus the model based on the model of aging by Arlt, explaining fatigue by the simple orientation of defect dipoles along the polarization axis (see Section 2.3.3) is unlikely because it does not imply any change in the defect concentration but only a simple migration of oxygen vacancies in the unit cell. As shown above, the defects responsible for fatigue are thermally very stable. This may be ascribed to deeply trapped electronic charge carriers or to ionic species. Several experimental results reported in the literature (see Section 2.3.2) show that trapped electronic charge carriers are able to pin domains. The reflectance measurements reported here show that electronic charge carriers are involved in fatigue. Ionic species, and particularly their vacancies, may also be responsible for domain pinning as reported in several fatigue models (see Section 2.3.3). There is a fairly large body of evidence in the literature that oxygen vacancies, which are the most mobile defects at room temperature, play a relevant role in fatigue but no unequivocal evidence has been brought forward so far. Furthermore, defects may agglomerate and find very stable energetic arrangements in clusters, stabilizing the domain system, as was mentioned in several models [14, 15, 11, 143]. This would also explain the high thermal stability of the polarization degradation.

It is clear that bipolar cycling induces much more stable defects than unipolar cycling. Thus, the fact that the polarization is reversed in the bipolar case must provide a driving force which leads to the creation and/or motion of defects. Most of the fatigue models explain the drift of defects by fields which are equal or slightly higher than the applied field. However the applied field is negligible in comparison to the depolarizing field. The idea of Lupascu seems to be the most plausible [11]. He argues that the driving force for defect migration comes from the local depolarizing field, which is unscreened during small fractions of time during a bipolar cycle just before the domain system switches.

Several mechanisms can be proposed in order to account for the dominant role of the near electrode region in fatigue for the material investigated in this work. A possibility is that there is an oxidation of the electrodes at the interface with the ferroelectric [203]. The adsorption of oxygen atoms onto the electrode surface would yield an increasing number of oxygen vacancies in the near electrode region, which may migrate, agglomerate and pin the domains. Another possibility is that silver atoms diffuse into the ferroelectric during the burning-in of the electrodes at 850 °C. Silver ions could substitute some lead ions or fill some lead vacancies and act as acceptors, therefore increasing the concentration of oxygen vacancies. A charge injection from the electrode through a Schottky emission and subsequent trapping of electronic charges at deep levels or charge accumulation at polarization discontinuities may also play a role in fatigue. Microcracks originating underneath the electrodes because of stress discontinuities may also play an indirect role in fatigue as mentioned above.

The measurements after polishing show that switching probably starts from the electrodes and propagates into the bulk. When fatigue reaches a certain point in the near electrode region, the grains located there delay the switching of the whole sample so that the bulk does not switch before the field is reversed. From this point on, only the grains close to the electrodes switch and the rest of the sample not. So the fatigue increases more and more in the near electrode region and not in the bulk.

Chapter 6

Summary

In the present study, some aspects of the effects of unipolar cycling and bipolar cycling in a commercial bulk lead zirconate titanate were investigated.

Unipolar as well as bipolar polarization and strain hysteresis loops were acquired after unipolar cycling of up to $1 \cdot 10^9$ cycles at 2 E_c. The bipolar measurements after cycling show a small decrease in the remanent polarization and an increasing asymmetry of the strain hysteresis with cycle number, which is explained by an offset polarization. Under high bipolar fields, the offsets are fairly stable and large numbers of bipolar cycles at $2E_c$ are needed to re-establish symmetry of the strain hysteresis. Since the removal of this offset polarization under consecutive bipolar cycles is accompanied by a regain of switchable polarization, this offset polarization was assigned to pinned domains. Thermal annealing, on the other hand, permits a recovery of symmetry at a fairly low temperature.

Fast switching measurements show a retardation of polarization reversal after unipolar cycling, which is removed after one single switching. This indicates that trapped electronic charge carriers are the most probable candidates for domain pinning.

The results suggest that different mechanisms are responsible for unipolar and bipolar fatigue. Unipolar fatigue is proposed to be caused by the redistribution of trapped charge carriers which are liberated during switching and redistributed at polarization discontinuities. This yields a screening of some domains and hinders their switching.

Electrical and microstructural investigations of the same material after bipolar cycling were also conducted.

Impedance spectroscopy was used to characterize the electrical microstructure of the material after fatigue. Relaxation responses were observed at temperatures above T_c. The fresh sample exhibited a single response in the Z and M formalisms which was associated with the bulk. An additional response, corresponding to an electroactive region induced by fatigue, was observed in the fatigued sample in the M formalism. At high temperature this region has a higher capacitance than the bulk.

After polishing the near electrode region of fatigued samples and re-electroding, the switching behavior was mostly recovered and the second response observed by impedance spectroscopy vanished, indicating that the near electrode region is largely responsible for fatigue in the sample. Fatigue yielded a decrease of the capacitance of this layer indicating an increase in its thickness, which correlated with the polarization loss observed in the corresponding hysteresis loops.

Fast switching measurements showed that a strong delay in polarization reversal is induced, extending over more than ten orders of magnitude in time. This delay cannot be accounted for by the classical theory of switching. After an extended period of time, the polarization reaches saturation, indicating that fatigue must be seen as a retardation of the polarization reversal. A stretched exponential function is found to yield the best fit of the switching profile. Several microscopic mechanisms are discussed in order to explain this effect for a polycrystalline material: voltage drop through an interface layer, random fields induced by ionizations during bipolar cycling, clustering of point defects, and cascaded switching on the scale of the microstructure.

Thermal annealing was found to yield only a partial recovery of the switching behavior correlated with a decrease of the fatigue-induced response observed in the impedance spectra. The recovery differs from that yielded by polishing the near electrode region and only affects the slow switching components. The steps observed in the recovery at different temperatures indicate that several mechanisms and defects, with different activation energies, are responsible for fatigue.

Reflectance spectroscopy data acquired in the bulk of the sample showed that fatigue yields a strong increase in optical absorption over a wide range of frequencies, from the ultraviolet to the near-infrared. This absorption may be associated with the occupation of shallow traps located close to the band edges.

The most popular models of fatigue were then discussed. For this particular composition, a domain wall pinning mechanism seems to be the most realistic scenario. Scenarios involving oxidation of the electrodes at the interface with the ferroelectric, diffusion of silver into the bulk, charge carriers injection through the electrodes or an indirect effect of microcracks are possible explanations for the occurrence of fatigue dominant in the near electrode regions.

Bibliography

[1] A. S. Sonin and B. A. Strukow. *Einführung in die Ferroelektrizität.* Akademie Verlag, Berlin, 1974.

[2] Yuhuan Xu. *Ferroelectric Materials and Their Applications.* Elsevier Science Publishers B.V., Amsterdam, 1991.

[3] D. Damjanovic. Ferroelectric, dielectric and piezoelectric properties of ferroelectric thin films and ceramics. *Rep. Prog. Phys.*, 61:1267–1324, 1998.

[4] J. F. Nye. *Physical Properties of Crystals.* Oxford Science Publications, Clarendon Press, Oxford, 1985.

[5] M. E. Lines and A. M. Glass. *Principles and Applications of Ferroelectrics and related Materials.* Clarendon Press, Oxford, 1977.

[6] V. Ya. Shur. Fast polarization reversal process: Evolution of ferroelectric domain structure in thin films. In *Ferroelectric Thin Films: Synthesis and Basic Properties, C. Paz de Araujo, J.F. Scott, G.W. Taylor, Eds., Ferroelectricity and Related Phenomena, Vol. 10, Gordon and Breach, Amsterdam*, pages 153–192, 1996.

[7] Y. Ishibashi and Y. Takagi. Note on ferroelectric domain switching. *J. Phys. Soc. Jpn.*, 31:506–510, 1971.

[8] L. E.. Cross. *Ferroelectric ceramics: tailoring properties for specific applications. In Setter, N. Colla, E. L., Ferroelectric Ceramics.* Birkhäuser Verlag, Basel, Boston, Berlin, 1993.

[9] R. Waser and D. M. Smyth. Defect chemistry, conduction and breakdown mechanism of perovskite-structure titanates. In *Ferroelectric Thin Films: Synthesis and Basic Properties, C. Paz de Araujo, J.F. Scott, G.W. Taylor, Eds., Ferroelectricity and Related Phenomena, Vol. 10, Gordon and Breach, Amsterdam*, pages 47–92, 1996.

[10] D. M. Smyth. Defects and order in perovskite-related oxides. *Ann. Rev. Mater. Sci.*, 15:329–357, 1985.

[11] D. C. Lupascu. *Fatigue in Ferroelectric Ceramics and Related Issues.* Springer, Berlin, Heidelberg, 2003.

[12] N. Setter Ed. *Piezoelectric Material in Devices.* N. Setter,EPFL Swiss Federal Institute of Technology Lausanne, Switzerland, 2002.

[13] W. J. Merz and J. R. Anderson. Ferroelectric storage device. *Bell lab. Rec.*, 33:335–342, 1955.

[14] C. Brennan. Model of ferroelectric fatigue due to defect/domain interactions. *Ferroelectrics*, 150:199–208, 1993.

[15] In-K. Yoo and S. B. Desu. Mechanism of fatigue in ferroelectric thin films. *phys. stat. sol. (a)*, 133:565–573, 1992.

[16] T. Mihara, H. Watanabe, and C. A. Paz de Araujo. Polarization fatigue characteristics of sol-gel ferroelectric $Pb(Zr_{0.4}Ti_{0.6})O_3$ thin-film capacitors. *Jpn. J. Appl. Phys.*, 33, part 1, 7A:3996–4002, 1994.

[17] J. Nuffer, D. C. Lupascu, and J. Rödel. Damage evolution in ferroelectric PZT induced by bipolar electric cycling. *Acta Mater.*, 48:3783–3794, 2000.

[18] CZ. Pawlaczyk, A. K. Tagantsev, K. Brooks, I. M. Reaney, R. Klissurska, and N. Setter. Fatigue, rejuvenation and self-restoring in ferroelectric thin films. *Integrated Ferroelectrics*, 8:293–316, 1995.

[19] E. L. Colla, A. K. Tagantsev, A. L. Kholkin, and N. Setter. *dc*-voltage and cycling induced recovery of switched polarisation in fatigued ferroelectric thin film. *Integrated Ferroelectrics*, 10:289–294, 1995.

[20] K. Khatchaturyan. Mechanical fatigue in thin films induced by piezoelectric strains as a cause of ferroelectric fatigue. *J. Appl. Phys.*, 77:6449–6455, 1995.

[21] Q. Jiang, W. Cao, and L. E. Cross. Electric fatigue in lead zirconate titanate ceramics. *J. Am. Ceram. Soc.*, 77:211–215, 1994.

[22] W. L. Warren, B. A. Tuttle, and D. Dimos. Ferroelectric fatigue in perovskite oxides. *Appl. Phys. Lett.*, 67:1426–1428, 1995.

[23] E. Paton, M. Brazier, S. Mansour, and A. Bement. A critical study of defect migration and ferroelectric fatigue in lead zirconate titanate thin film capacitors under extreme temperatures. *Integrated Ferroelectrics*, 18:29–37, 1997.

[24] W. Pan, C. F. Yue, and O. Tosyali. Fatigue of ferroelectric polarization and the electric field induced strain in lead lanthanum zirconate titanate ceramics. *J. Am. Ceram. Soc.*, 75:1534–1540, 1992.

[25] V. Bobnar, Z. Kutnjak, A. Levstik, J. Holc, M. Kosec, T. Hauke, R. Steinhausen, and H. Beige. Correlation between fatigue and piezoelectric properties in (Pb,La)(Zr,Ti)O_3 thick films. *J. Appl. Phys.*, 85:622–624, 1999.

[26] E. L. Colla, A. L. Kholkin, D. Taylor, A. K. Tagantsev, K. G. Brooks, and N. Setter. Characterisation of the fatigued state of ferroelectric PZT thin-film capacitors. *Microelectronic Engin.*, 29:145–148, 1995.

[27] H. Weitzing, G. A. Schneider, J. Steffens, M. Hammer, and M. J. Hoffmann. Cyclic fatigue due to electric loading in ferroelectric ceramics. *J. Eur. Ceram. Soc.*, 19:1333–1337, 1999.

[28] A. L. Kholkin, E. L. Colla, A. K. Tagantsev, D. V. Taylor, and N. Setter. Fatigue of piezoelectric properties in Pb(Zr,Ti)O_3 films. *Appl. Phys. Lett.*, 68:2577–2579, 1996.

[29] Donny Wang, Y. Fotinich, and G. P. Carman. Influence of temperature on the electromechanical and fatigue behaviour of piezoelectric ceramics. *J. Appl. Phys.*, 83:5342–5350, 1998.

[30] T. Mihara, H. Watanabe, and C. A. Paz de Araujo. Characteristic change due to polarization fatigue of sol-gel ferroelectric Pb(Zr$_{0.4}$Ti$_{0.6}$)O_3 thin-film capacitors. *Jpn. J. Appl. Phys.*, 33:5281–5286, 1994.

[31] J. F. Scott, C. A. Paz de Araujo, B. M. Melnick, L. D. McMillan, and R. Zuleeg. Quantitative measurement of space- charge effects in lead zirconate- titanate memories. *J. Appl. Phys.*, 70:382–388, 1991.

[32] I. Stolichnov, A. Tagantsev, N. Setter, J. S. Cross, and M. Tsukada. Degradation of asymmetrical Pt/SRO/PLZT/Pt capacitors: Role of Pt and oxide electrodes. *Integrated Ferroelectrics*, 26:1013–1023, 1999.

[33] Q. Jiang, E. C. Subbarao, and L. E. Cross. Grain size dependence of electric fatigue behavior of hot pressed PLZT ferroelectric ceramics. *Acta metall. mater.*, 42:3687–3694, 1994.

[34] In-K. Yoo and B. Seshu Desu. Fatigue modeling of lead zirconate titanate thin films. *Mater. Sci. & Engin. B*, 13:319–322, 1992.

[35] M. Grossmann, D. Bolten, O. Lohse, U. Boettger, R. Waser, and S. Tiedke. Correlation between switching and fatigue in $PbZr_{0.3}Ti_{0.7}O_3$ thin films. *Appl. Phys. Lett.*, 77:1894–1896, 2000.

[36] G. White. private communication. 2000.

[37] A. Yu. Kudzin, T. V. Panchenko, and S. P. Yudın. Behavior of $180°$ domain walls of barium titanate single crystal during the "fatigue" and recovery of switching polarization. *Sov. Phys. Solid State*, 16:1589–1590, 1975.

[38] H. M. Duiker and P. D. Beale. Grain-size effect in ferroelectric switching. *Phys. Rev. B*, 41:490–495, 1990.

[39] B. M. Melnick, C. A. Paz de Araujo, L. D. McMillan, D. A. Carver, and J. F. Scott. Recent results on switching, fatigue and electrical characterization of sol- gel based PZT capacitors. *Ferroelectrics*, 116:79–93, 1991.

[40] C. J. Brennan, R. D. Parrella, and D. E. Larsen. Temperature dependent fatigue rates in thin- film ferroelectric capacitors. *Ferroelectrics*, 151:33–38, 1994.

[41] Q. Y. Jiang, E. C. Subbarao, and L. E. Cross. Effect of composition and temperature on electric fatigue of La-doped lead zirconate titanate ceramics. *J. Appl. Phys.*, 75:7433–7443, 1994.

[42] R. Ramesh, W. K. Chan, B. Wilkens, H. Gilchrist, T. Sands, J. M. Tarascon, V. G. Keramidas, D. K. Fork, J. Lee, and A. Safari. Fatigue and aging in ferroelectric $PbZr_{0.2}Ti_{0.8}O_3/YBa_2Cu_3O_7$ heterostructures. *Integrated Ferroelectrics*, 1:1–15, 1992.

[43] K. Lee, B. R. Rhee, and C. Lee. Characteristics of ferroelectric $Pb(Zr,Ti)O_3$ thin films having Pt/PtO_x electrode barriers. *Appl. Phys. Lett*, 79:821–823, 2001.

[44] S. B. Majumder, D. C. Agrawal, Y. N. Mohapatra, and R. S. Katiyar. Fatigue and dielectric properties of undoped and Ce doped PZT thin films. *Integrated Ferroelectrics*, 29:63–74, 2000.

[45] E. L. Colla, D. V. Taylor, A. K. Tagantsev, and N. Setter. Discrimination between bulk and interface scenarios for the suppression of the switchable polarization (fatigue) in $Pb(Zr,Ti)O_3$ thin films capacitors with Pt electrodes. *Appl. Phys. Lett.*, 72:2478–2480, 1998.

[46] N. Zhang, L. Li, and Z. Gui. Frequency dependence of ferroelectric fatigue in PLZT ceramics. *J. Eur. Ceram. Soc.*, 21:677–681, 2001.

[47] Q. Y. Jiang, Wenwu Cao, and L. E. Cross. Electric fatigue initiated by surface contamination in high polarization ceramics. In *IEEE Proceedings of the 8th International Symposium on Applications of Ferroelectrics, Aug.*, pages 107–110, 1992.

[48] Q. Jiang and L. E. Cross. Effect of porosity on electrical fatigue behavior in PLZT and PZT ceramics. *J. Mater. Sci.*, 28:4536–4543, 1993.

[49] Q. Y. Jiang, E. C. Subbarao, and L. E. Cross. Fatigue in PLZT: Acoustic emission as a discriminator between microcracking and domain switching. *Ferroelectrics*, 154:113–118, 1994.

[50] Wen-Jen Lin, Tseng-Yuen Tseng, Shuen-Perg Lin, Shun-Lih Tu, Hong Chang, Sheng-Jenn Yang, and I-Nan Lin. Influence of crystal structure on the fatigue properties of $Pb_{1-x}La_x(Zr_yTi_z)O_3$ thin films prepared by pulsed-laser deposition technique. *J. Am. Ceram. Soc.*, 80:1065–1072, 1997.

[51] F. Yan, P. Bao, H. L. W. Chan, C-L Choy, X. Chen, J. Zhu, and Y Wang. Effect of grain size on the fatigue properties of $Pb(Zr_{0.3}Ti_{0.7})O_3$ thin films prepared by metallorganic decomposition. *Ferroelectrics.*, 252:209–216, 2001.

[52] Jang-Sik Lee, Chan-Soo Kim, and Seung-Ki Joo. Fatigue and data retention characteristics of single-grained $Pb(Zr,Ti)O_3$ thin films. In *IEEE Proc. 12th Intern. Symp. on the Applic. of Ferroelectrics, ISAF2000*, pages 595–598, 2000.

[53] D. E. Dausch. Ferroelectric polarization fatigue in PZT-based RAINBOWs and bulk ceramics. *J. Am. Ceram. Soc.*, 80:2355–2360, 1997.

[54] W. Y. Pan, C. F. Yue, and B. A. Tuttle. Ferroelectric fatigue in modified bulk lead zirconate titanate ceramics and thin films. In *Ceramic Transactions, Ferroelectric Films, A.S. Bhalla, K.M. Nair, Eds.*, volume 25, pages 385–397, 1992.

[55] B. Güttler, U. Bismayer, P. Groves, and E. Salje. Fatigue mechanisms in thin film PZT memory materials. *Semicond. Sci. Technol.*, 10:245–248, 1995.

[56] J. Nuffer, D. C. Lupascu, A. Glazounov, H. J. Kleebe, and J. Rödel. Microstructural modifications of ferroelectric lead zirconate titanate ceramics due to bipolar electric fatigue. *J. Eur. Ceram. Soc.*, 22:2133–2142, 2002.

[57] H. Nagata, H. Haneda, I. Sakaguchi, T. Takenaka, and J. Tanaka. Reaction and diffusion between PLZT ceramics and Ag electrode. *J. Ceram. Soc. Jpn.*, 105:862–867, 1997.

[58] T. Kamiya, T. Tsurumi, and M. Daimon. Quantum calculation of molecular orbitals for PZT solid solutions by DVXα cluster method. In *Computer Aided Innovation of New Materials II, M. Doyama, J. Kihara, M. Tanaka, R. Yamamoto (Editors)*, pages 225–228, 1993.

[59] Dage Liu, Chen Wang, Hongxi Zhang, Junwei Li, Liancheng Zhao, and Chunli Bai. Domain configuration and interface structure analysis of sol-gel-derived PZT ferroelectric thin films. *Surf. Interf. Anal.*, 32:27–31, 2001.

[60] S. B. Majumder, B. Roy, R. S. Katiyar, and S. B. Krupanidhi. Improvement of the degradation chararacteristics of sol-gel derived PZT(53/47) thin films : Effect of conventional and graded iron doping. *Integrated Ferroelectrics.*, 39:127–136, 2001.

[61] W. I. Lee, J. K. Lee, I. S. Chung, C. W. Chung, and I. K. Yoo. *Patent No. US5625529.*

[62] T. Ijima, G. He, Z. Wang, H. Tsuboi, K. Hiyama, and M. Okada. Ferroelectric properties of Al-doped lead titanate zirconate thin films prepared by chemical solution deposition process. *Jpn. j. Appl. Phys.*, 39:5426–5428, 2000.

[63] K. G. Klissurska, K. G. Brooks, and N. Setter. Acceptor dopant effects on endurance of PZT thin films. *Ferroelectrics*, 225:977–984, 1999.

[64] E.M. Giswold, M. Sayer, D. T. Amm, and I. D. Calder. The influence of niobium-doping on lead zirconate titanate ferroelectric thin-films. *Can. J. Phys.*, 69:260–264, 1991.

[65] K. Aoki and Y. Fukuda. The effects of La and Nb modification on fatigue and retention properties of $Pb(Ti, Zr)O_3$ thin-film capacitors. *Jpn. J. Appl. Phys.*, 36:1195–1197, 1997.

[66] D. F. Jr. Ryder and N. K. Raman. Sol-gel processing of Nb-doped $Pb(Zr, Ti)O_3$ thin-films for ferroelectric memory applications. *J. Electron. Mater.*, 21:971–975, 1992.

[67] J. Chen, M. P. Harmer, and D. M. Smyth. Compositional control of ferroelectric fatigue in perovskite ferroelectric ceramics and thin films. *J. Appl. Phys.*, 76:5394–5398, 1994.

[68] S. Priya, H. W. Kim, J. Ryu, K. Uchino, and D. Viehland. Fractal cluster modeling of the fatigue behavior of lead zirconate titanate. *Appl. Phys. Letters*, 80:1625–1627, 2002.

[69] J-K. Yang, W. S. Kim, and H. H. Park. The effect of excess Pb content on the crystallization and electrical properties in sol-gel derived $Pb(Zr_{0.4}, Ti_{0.6})O_3$ thin films. *Thin Solid Films.*, 377:739–744, 2000.

[70] Z. Song, J. Gao, X. Zhu, L. Wang, and C. Lin. Effects of excess Pb on structural and electrical properties of $Pb(Zr_{0.48}, Ti_{0.52})O_3$ thin films using MOD process. *J. Mater. Science*, 36:4285–4289, 2001.

[71] H. Doi and T. Atsuki. Influence of buffer layers and excess Pb/(Zr+Ti) ratios on fatigue characteristics of sol-gel-derived $Pb(Zr,Ti)O_3$ thin films. *Jpn. J. Appl. Phys. Part I*, 34(9B):5105–5112, 1995.

[72] Xiaofeng Du and I-Wei Chen. Fatigue of $Pb(Zr_{0.58}Ti_{0.47})O_3$ ferroelectric thin films. *J. Appl. Phys.*, 83:7789–7798, 1998.

[73] S. Pöykkö and D. J. Chadi. First principle study of Pb vacancies in $PbTiO_3$. *Appl. Phys. Lett.*, 76:499–501, 2000.

[74] H. Kanaya, T. Iwamoto, Y. Takahagi, I. Kunishima, and S. Tanaka. Hydrogen induced imprint mechanism of Pt/PZT/Pt capacitors by low-temperature hydrogen treatment. *Integrated Ferroelectrics*, 25:235–244, 1999.

[75] N. Zhang, L. Li, and Z. Gui. Improvement of electric fatigue properties in $Pb_{0.94}La_{0.4}(Zr_{0.70}, Ti_{0.30})O_3$ ferroelectric capacitors due to $SrBi_2Nb_2O_9$ incorporation. *Mater. Res. Bull.*, 36:2553–2562, 2001.

[76] N. Zhang, L. Li, and Z. Gui. Improvement of electric fatigue properties in PLZT ferroelectric ceramics due to $SrBi_2Ta_2O_9$ incorporation. *Materials Science and Engineering*, B90:185–190, 2002.

[77] N. Zhang, L. Li, and Z. Gui. Improvement of electric fatigue properties in PLZT ferroelectric capacitors due to zirconia incorporation. *Mater. Chem. Phys.*, 72:5–10, 2001.

[78] D. H. Kang, Y. J. Maeng, S. H. Shin, J. H. Park, and K. H. Yoon. Crystal structure, microstructure and ferroelectric properties of PZT(55/45) and PZT(80/20) thin films due to various buffer layers. *Ferroelectrics.*, 260:125–130, 2001.

[79] S. R. Shannigrahi and H. M. Jang. Fatigue-free lead zirconate titanate-based ca-
    pacitors for nonvolatile memories. *Appl. Phys. Letters*, 79:1051–1053, 2001.

[80] D. Bao, N. Wakiya, K. Shinozaki, and N. Mizutani. Preparation and electrical
    properties of $(Bi,La)_4Ti_3O_{12}/Pb(Zr, Ti)O_3/(Bi,La)_4Ti_3O_{12}$ multilayer thin films by
    a chemical solution deposition. *Ferroelectrics*, 270:27–32, 2002.

[81] H. K. Kim and N. A. Basit. Ferroelectric nonvolatile memory field-effect transis-
    tors based on a novel buffer layer structure. *International Journal of High Speed
    Electronics and Systems*, 10:39–46, 2000.

[82] A. Gruverman, O. Auciello, and H. Tokumoto. Nanoscale investigation of fatigue
    effect in $Pb(Zr,Ti)O_3$ films. *Appl. Phys. Lett.*, 69:3191–3193, 1996.

[83] E. L. Colla, S. Hong, D. V. Taylor, A. K. Tagantsev, and N. Setter. Direct ob-
    servation of region by region suppression of the switchable polarization (fatigue) in
    $Pb(Zr,Ti)O_3$ thin film capacitors with Pt electrodes. *Appl. Phys. Lett.*, 72:2763–
    2765, 1998.

[84] D. C. Lupascu and U. Rabe. Cyclic cluster growth in ferroelectric perovskites. *Phys.
    Rev. Lett.*, 89:187601, 2002.

[85] A. Krishnan, M. M. J. Treacy, M. E. Bisher, P. Chandra, and P. B. Littlewood.
    Efficient switching and domain interlocking observed in polyaxial ferroelectrics. *In-
    tegrated Ferroelectrics*, 43:31–49, 2002.

[86] C.-C. Chou, C.-S. Hou, and H.C. Pan. Domain boundary pinning and nucleation
    of ferroelectric $(Pb_{1-x}Sr_x)TiO_3$. *Ferroelectrics.*, 261:185–190, 2001.

[87] D. M. Smyth. Ionic transport in ferroelectrics. *Ferroelectrics*, 151:115–124, 1994.

[88] S. D. Bernstein, Y. Kisler, J. M. Wahl, S. E. Bernacki, and S. R. Collins. Effects of
    stoichiometry on PZT thin film capacitor properties. *Mater. Res. Soc. Symp. Proc.*,
    243:373–378, 1992.

[89] M. Brazier, S. Mansour, and M. McElfresh. Ferroelectric fatigue of $Pb(Zr,Ti)O_3$
    thin films measured in atmospheres of varying oxygen concentration. *Appl. Phys.
    Lett.*, 74:4032–4033, 1999.

[90] M. J. Pan, S. E. Park, K. A. Markowski, S. Yoshikawa, and C. A. Randall. Super-
    oxidation and electrochemical reactions during switching in $Pb(Zr,Ti)O_3$ ceramics.
    J. Am. Ceram. Soc., 79:2971–2974, 1996.

[91] D-C. Kim and W-J. Lee. Effect of LaNiO$_3$ top electrode on the resistance of Pb(Zr,Ti)O$_3$ ferroelectric capacitor to hydrogen damage and fatigue. *Jpn. J. Appl. Phys.*, 41:1470–1476, 2002.

[92] W. Wu, K. H. Wong, and Y. H. Zhang. Top-interface-controlled fatigue of epitaxial Pb(Zr$_{0.52}$, Ti$_{0.48}$)O$_3$ ferroelectric thin films on La$_{0.7}$Sr$_{0.3}$Mn$_{0.3}$ electrodes. *Appl. Phys. Lett*, 77:3441–3443, 2000.

[93] J. Nuffer, M. Schröder, D. C. Lupascu, and J. Rödel. Negligible oxygen liberation during the fatigue of lead-zirconate-titanate. *Appl. Phys. Lett.*, 79(22):3675–3677, 2001.

[94] L. F. Schloss, P. C. McIntyre, B. C. Hendrix, S. M. Bilodeau, J. F. Roeder, and S. R. Gilbert. Oxygen tracer studies of ferroelectric fatigue in Pb(Zr,Ti)O$_3$ thin films. *Appl. Phys. Lett*, 81:3218–3220, 2002.

[95] D. Dimos, W.L. Warren, M.B. Sinclair, B.A. Tuttle, and R.W. Schwartz. Photoinduced hysteresis changes and optical storage in (Pb,La)(Zr,Ti)O$_3$ thin films and ceramics. *J. Appl. Phys.*, 76:4305–4315, 1994.

[96] W. L. Warren and D. Dimos. Photoinduced hysteresis changes and charge trapping in BaTiO$_3$ dielectrics. *Appl. Phys. Lett.*, 64:866–868, 1994.

[97] W. L. Warren, D. Dimos, B. A. Tuttle, G. E. Pike, and H. N. Al-Shareef. Relationships among ferroelectric fatigue, electronic charge trapping, defect-dipoles, and oxygen vacancies in perovskite oxides. *Integrated Ferroelectrics*, 16:77–86, 1997.

[98] W. L. Warren, J. Robertson, D.B. Dimos, B.A. Tuttle, and D.M. Smyth. Transient hole traps in PZT. *Ferroelectrics*, 153:303–308, 1994.

[99] S. Lenjer, O. F. Schirmer, H. Hesse, and Th. W. Kool. Conduction states in oxide perovskites: three manifestations of Ti^{3+} Jahn-Teller polarons in barium titanate. *Phys. Rev. B*, 66:165106, 2002.

[100] J. F. Scott and M. Dawber. Physics of ferroelectric thin-film memory devices. *Ferroelectrics*, 265:119–128, 2002.

[101] J. Lee, S. Esayan, A. Safari, and R. Ramesh. Fatigue and photoresponse of lead zirconate titanate thin film capacitors. *Integrated Ferroelectrics*, 6:289–300, 1995.

[102] H. N. Al-Shareef, D. Dimos, W. L. Warren, and B. A. Tuttle. A model for optical and electrical polarization fatigue in SrBi$_2$Ta$_2$O$_9$ and Pb(Zr,Ti)O$_3$. *Integrated Ferroelectrics*, 15:53–67, 1997.

[103] C. R. Peterson, S. A. Mansour, and A. Bement, Jr. Effects of optical illumination on fatigued lead zirconate titanate capacitors. *Integrated Ferroelectrics*, 7:139–147, 1995.

[104] S. A. Mansour and R. W. Vest. The dependence of ferroelectric and fatigue behaviors of PZT films on microstructure and orientation. *Integrated Ferroelectrics*, 1:57–69, 1992.

[105] W. S. Kim, J-K. Yang, and H. H. Park. Influence of preferred orientation of lead zirconate titanate thin film on the ferroelectric properties. *Applied Surface Science*, 169-170:549–552, 2001.

[106] K. Takemura, M. Ozgul, V. Bornard, and S. Trolier-McKinstry. Fatigue anisotropy in single crystal $Pb(Zn_{1/3}Nb_{2/3})O_3$-$PbTiO_3$. *J. Appl. Phys.*, 88:7272–7277, 2000.

[107] F. Chu and G. Fox. Relationship between the PB content, crystallographic texture and ferroelectric properties of PLZT thin films for FRAM applications. *Integrated. Ferroelectrics*, 33:19–26, 2001.

[108] C. J. Brennan. Defect chemistry model of the ferroelectric-electrode interface. *Integrated Ferroelectrics*, 7:93–109, 1995.

[109] I. Stolichnov, A. Tagantsev, E. L. Colla, and N. Setter. Tunneling conduction in virgin and fatigued states of PZT films. *Ferroelectrics*, 225:125–132, 1999.

[110] Q. Jiang, E. C. Subbarao, and L. E. Cross. Effects of electrodes and electroding methods on fatigue behavior in ferroelectric materials. *Ferroelectrics*, 154:119–124, 1994.

[111] W. Y. Pan, C. Q. Dam, Q. M. Zhang, and L. E. Cross. Large displacement transducers based on electric field forced phase transitions in the tetragonal $(Pb_{0.97}La_{0.02})(Ti,Zr,Sn)O_3$ family of ceramics. *J. Appl. Phys.*, 66:6014–6023, 1989.

[112] S. Thakoor. Enhanced fatigue and retention in ferroelectric thin film memory capacitors by post-top-electrode anneal treatment. *J. Appl. Phys.*, 75:5409–5414, 1994.

[113] S. D. Bernstein, T. Y. Wong, Y. Kisler, and R. W. Tustison. Fatigue of ferroelectric $PbZr_xTi_yO_3$ capacitors with Ru and RuO_x electrodes. *J. Mater. Res.*, 8:12–13, 1993.

[114] R. Ramesh and V. G. Keramidas. Metal-oxide heterostructures. *Annu. Rev. Mater. Sci.*, 25:647–678, 1995.

[115] R. Ramesh, W. K. Chan, B. Wilkens, H. Gilchrist, T. Sands, J. M. Tarascon, V. G. Keramidas, D. K. Fork, J. Lee, and A. Safari. Fatigue and retention in ferroelectric Y-Ba-CuO/Pb-Zr-TiO/Y-Ba-Cu-O heterostructures. *Appl. Phys. Lett.*, 61:1537–1539, 1992.

[116] T. Hase, T. Noguchi, K. Takemura, and Y. Miyasaka. Fatigue characteristics of PZT capacitors with Ir/IrO$_x$ electrodes. In *Proc. 11th IEEE Int. Symp. Appl. Ferroel. IEEE-cat.# 98CH36245*, pages 7–10, 1998.

[117] Sang-Mo Koo, Li-Rong Zheng, and R. V. Rao. BaRuO$_3$ thin film electrode for ferroelectric lead zirconate titanate capacitors. *J. Mater. Res.*, 14:3833–3836, 1999.

[118] H. N. Al-Shareef, B. A. Tuttle, W. L. Warren, T. J. Headley, D. Dimos, J. A. Voigt, and R. D. Nasby. Effect of B-site cation stochiometry on electrical fatigue of RuO$_2$/Pb(Zr$_x$Ti$_{1-x}$)O$_3$/RuO$_2$ capacitors. *J. Appl. Phys.*, 79:1013–1016, 1996.

[119] A. K. Tagantsev, I. Stolichnov, E. L. Colla, and N. Setter. Polarization fatigue in ferroelectric films: Basic experimental findings, phenomenological scenarios, and microscopic features. *J. Appl. Phys.*, 90:1387–1402, 2001.

[120] D. Dimos, H. N. Al-Shareef, W. L. Warren, and B. A. Tuttle. Photoinduced changes in the fatigue behavior of SrBi$_2$Ta$_2$O$_9$ and Pb(Zr,Ti)O$_3$ films. *J. Appl. Phys.*, 80:1682–1687, 1996.

[121] Xiaofeng Du and I-Wei Chen. Model experiments on fatigue of Pb(Zr$_{0.53}$Ti$_{0.47}$)O$_3$ ferroelectric thin films. *Appl. Phys. Lett.*, 72:1923–1925, 1998.

[122] Active material Laboratories. http://aml.seas.ucla.edu/home.htm.

[123] H. Cao and A. G. Evans. Electric-field-induced fatigue crack growth in piezo-electrics. *J. Am. Ceram. Soc.*, 77:1783–1786, 1994.

[124] W. R. Salaneck. Some fatiguing effects in 8/65/35 PLZT fine grained ferroelectric ceramic. *Ferroelectrics*, 4:97–101, 1972.

[125] K. Carl. Ferroelectric properties and fatiguing effects of modified PbTiO$_3$ ceramics. *Ferroelectrics*, 9:23–32, 1975.

[126] J. Nuffer. *Schädigungsmechanismen in ferroelektrischer PZT-Keramik unter bipolare elektrischer Zyklierung*. VDI Verlag, Düsseldorf, 2001.

[127] S. J. Kim and Q. Jiang. Microcracking and electrical fatigue of polycrystalline ferroelectric ceramics. *Smart Mater. Struct.*, 5:321–326, 1996.

[128] W. L. Warren, D. Dimos, B. A. Tuttle, G. E. Pike, R. W. Schwartz, P. J. Clews, and D. C. McIntyre. Polarization suppression in Pb(Zr,Ti)O$_3$ thin films. *J. Appl. Phys.*, 77:6695–6701, 1995.

[129] W. L. Warren, D. Dimos, B. A. Tuttle, G. E. Pike, M. V. Raymond, R. D. Nasby, and J. T. Evans, Jr. Mechanisms for the suppression of the switchable polarization in PZT and BaTiO$_3$. *Mater. Res. Soc. Symp. Proc.*, 361:51–65, 1995.

[130] J. Nuffer, D. C. Lupascu, and J. Rödel. Stability of pinning centers in fatigued lead-zirconate-titanate. *Appl. Phys. Lett.*, 80(6):1049–1051, 2002.

[131] W. C. Stewart and L. S. Cosentino. Some optical and electrical switching characteristics of a lead zirconate titanate ferroelectric ceramic. *Ferroelectrics*, 1:149–167, 1970.

[132] J. F. Scott, B. Pouligny, K. Dimmler, M. Parris, D. Butler, and S. Eaton. Activation field, fatigue, and waiting-time effect in KNO$_3$ thin-film memories. *J. Appl. Phys.*, 62:4510–4513, 1987.

[133] A. Levstik, M. Kosec, V. Bobnar, C. Filipic, and Janes Holc. Switching kinetics in thick film and bulk lead lanthanum zirconate titanate ceramics. *Jpn. J. Appl. Phys.*, 36:2744–2746, 1997.

[134] V. Ya. Shur, E. L. Rumyantsev, E. V. Nicolaeva, E. I. Shishkin, I. S. Baturin, D. C. Lupascu, C. A. Randall, and M. Ozgul. Kinetics of fatigue in bulk ferroelectrics. In *Smart Structures and Materials: Active Materials: Behavior and Mechanics, C. S. Lynch, Ed. Proc. SPIE*, page 4699, 2002.

[135] M. Tajiri and H. Nozawa. New fatigue model based on thermionic field emission mechanism. *Jpn. J. Appl. Phys.*, 40:5590–5594, 2001.

[136] M. Dawber and J. F. Scott. Fatigue and oxygen vacancy ordering in thin-film and bulk single crystal ferroelectris. *Integrated Ferroelectrics*, 32:259–266, 2001.

[137] G. Arlt and H. Neumann. Internal bias in ferroelectric ceramics: Origin and time dependence. *Ferroelectrics*, 87:109–120, 1988.

[138] R. Lohkämper, H. Neumann, and G. Arlt. Internal bias in acceptor-doped BaTiO$_3$ ceramics: Numerical evaluation of increase and decrease. *J. Appl. Phys.*, 68:4220–4224, 1990.

[139] G. Arlt and U. Robels. Aging and fatigue in bulk ferroelectric perovskite ceramics. *Integrated Ferroelectrics*, 3:343–349, 1993.

[140] S. Steinsvik, R. Bugge, J. Gjønnes, J. Taftø, and N. Truls. The defect structure of $SrTi_{1-x}Fe_xO_{3-y}$ ($x = 0 - 0.8$) investigated by electrical conductivity measurements and electron energy loss spectroscopy (EELS). *J. Phys. Chem. Solids*, 58:969–976, 1997.

[141] S. Pöykkö and D. J. Chadi. Dipolar defect model for fatigue in ferroelectric perowskites. *Phys. Rev. Lett.*, 83:1231–1234, 1999.

[142] In-K. Yoo and S. B. Desu. Fatigue and hysteresis modelling of ferroelectric materials. *J. Intell. Mater. Sys. Struct.*, 4:490–495, 1993.

[143] M. Dawber and J. Scott. A model for fatigue in ferroelectric perovskite thin films. *Appl. Phys. Lett.*, 76:1060–1062, 2000.

[144] J. F. Scott and M. Dawber. Oxygen-vacancy ordering as a fatigue mechanism in perovskite ferroelectrics. *Appl. Phys. Lett.*, 76:3801–3803, 2000.

[145] P. K. Larsen, G. J. M. Dormans, D. J. Taylor, and P. J. van Veldhoven. Ferroelectric properties and fatigue of $PbZr_{0.51}Ti_{0.49}O_3$ thin films of varying thickness: Blocking layer model. *J. Appl. Phys.*, 76:2405–2413, 1994.

[146] A. M. Bratkovsky and A. P. Levanyuk. Abrupt appearance of the domain pattern and fatigue of thin ferroelectric films. *Phys. Rev. Lett.*, 84:3177–3180, 2000.

[147] J. J. Lee, C. L. Thio, and S. B. Desu. Electrode contacts on ferroelectric $Pb(Zr_{(x)}Ti_{(1-x)})O_3$ and $SrBi_2Ta_2O_9$ thin films and their influence on fatigue properties. *J. Appl. Phys.*, 78:5073–5077, 1995.

[148] A. K. Tagantsev, M. Landivar, E. Colla, and N. Setter. Identification of passive layer in ferroelectric thin films from their switching parameters. *J. Appl. Phys.*, 78:2623–2630, 1995.

[149] A. K. Tagantsev, C. Z. Pawlaczyk, K. Brooks, M. Landivar, E. Colla, and N. Setter. Depletion and depolarizing effects in ferroelectric thin films and their manifestations in switching and fatigue. *Integrated Ferroelectrics*, 6:309–320, 1995.

[150] K. Miura and M. Tanaka. Origin of fatigue in ferroelectric perovskite oxides. *Jpn. J. Appl. Phys.*, 35:2719–2725, 1996.

[151] C. H. Park and D. J. Chadi. Microscopic study of oxygen-vacancy defects in ferroelectric perowskites. *Phys. Rev. B*, 57:R13961–R13964, 1998.

[152] V. C. Lo and Z. J. Chen. Modelling the roles of oxygen vacancies in thin film ferroelectric memory. In *ISAF 2000. Proceedings of the 12th IEEE Int. Symp. on Appl. of Ferroelectrics 2000 (IEEE Cat. No. 00CH37076)*, pages 157–160, 2001.

[153] S. J. Kim and Q. Jiang. Microcracking and fatigue of polycristalline ferroelectric ceramics. *The U.S. Office of Naval Research*, pages 1–13, 1995.

[154] K. Kachaturyan. Mechanical fatigue in thin films induced by piezoelectric strains as a cause of ferroelectric fatigue. *J. Appl. Phys.*, 77·6449–6455, 1995.

[155] H. M. Duiker, P. D. Beale, J. F. Scott, C. A. Paz de Araujo, B. M. Melnick, J. D. Cuchiaro, and L. D. McMillan. Fatigue and switching in ferroelectric memories: Theory and experiment. *J. Appl. Phys.*, 68:5783–5791, 1990.

[156] V. Ya. Shur, E. L. Rumyantsev, E. V. Nikolaeva, E. I. Shishkin, and I. S. Baturin. Kinetic approach to fatigue phenomenon in ferroelectrics. *J. Appl. Phys.*, 90:6312–6315, 2001.

[157] D. Ricinschi, A. I. Lerescu, and M. Okuyama. Investigation of fatigue mechanisms in Pb(Zr,Ti)O$_3$ films from a correlated analysis of hysteresis parameters in a lattice model with distributed polarization clamping. *Jpn. J. Appl. Phys.*, 39:L990–L992, 2000.

[158] V. Chikarmane, C. Sudhama, J. Kim, J. Lee, A. Tasch, and S. Novak. Effects of post-deposition annealing ambient on the electrical characteristics and phase transformation kinetics of sputtered lead zirconate titanate (65/35) thin film capacitors. *J. Vac. Sci.Technol. A*, 10:1562–1568, 1992.

[159] G. Helke and W. Kirsch. Dielektrische und Piezoelektrische Eigenschaften der ternären keramischen festen Lösungen Pb(Ni$_{1/3}$Sb$_{2/3}$)O$_3$-PbTiO$_3$-PbZrO$_3$. *Hermsdorfer Technische Mitteilungen*, 32:1010–1015, 1971.

[160] H. von Seggern and S. Fedosov. A novel displacement component in pvdf and its role in ferroelectric switching. *IEEE Trans. Diel. Electr. Insul.*, 7:543–550, 2000.

[161] *Agilent Technologies Impedance Measurement Handbook*. Agilent Technologies, 2000.

[162] D. C. Sinclair, F. D. Morrison, and A. West. Applications of combined impedance and electric modulus spectroscopy to characterise electroceramics. *International Ceramics*, Issue 2:33–38, 2000.

[163] D. C. Sinclair and A. West. Impedance and modulus spectroscopy of semiconducting BaTiO$_3$ showing positive temperature coefficient of resistance. *J. Appl. Phys.*, 66:3850–3856, 1989.

[164] S. Lucato. *Rissausbreitung in Blei-Zirkonat Titanat in Abhängigkeit des Polungszustands. Diplomarbeit TU Darmstadt.* 1999.

[165] G. Hunt. Spectral signature of particulate minerals in the visible and near infrared. *Geophysics*, 42:501–513, 1977.

[166] D. C. Lupascu, E. Aulbach, and J. Rödel. Mixed electromechanical fatigue in lead-zirconate-titanate ceramics. *J. Appl. Phys.*, 93:5551–5556, 2003.

[167] W. L. Warren, B. A. Tuttle, D. Dimos, G. E. Pike, H. N. Al-Shareef, R. Ramesh, and J. T. Evans, Jr. Imprint in ferroelectric capacitors. *Jpn. J. Appl. Phys.*, 35:1521–1524, 1996.

[168] T. Mihara, H. Watanabe, and C. A. Paz de Araujo. Evaluation of imprint properties in sol-gel ferroelectric Pb(ZrTi)O$_3$ thin-film capacitors. *Jpn. J. Appl. Phys.*, 32:4168–4174, 1993.

[169] J. Grindlay. *An Introduction to the Phenomenological Theory of Ferroelectrics.* Pergamon Press, Oxford, 1970.

[170] A. Furuta and K. Uchino. Dynamic observation of crack propagation in piezoelectric multilayer actuators. *J. Am. Ceram. Soc.*, 76:1615–1617, 1993.

[171] W. L. Warren, D. Dimos, and R. M. Waser. Degradation mechanism in ferroelectric and high-permittivity perovskites. *MRS Bulletin*, 21(7):40–45, 1996.

[172] U. Robels, L. Schneider-Störmann, and G. Arlt. Dielectric aging and its temperature dependence in ferroelectric ceramics. *Ferroelectrics*, 168:301–311, 1995.

[173] U. Robels and G. Arlt. Domain wall clamping in ferroelectrics by orientation of defects. *J. Appl. Phys.*, 73:3454–3460, 1993.

[174] N. Balke, H. Rauh, Y. A. Genenko, and D. C. Lupascu. A drift-diffusion model of ageing in ferroelectrics. *to be published.*

[175] W. L. Warren, D. Dimos, G. E. Pike, B. A. Tuttle, M. V. Raymond, R. Ramesh, and J. T. Evans, Jr. Voltage shifts and imprint in ferroelectric capacitors. *Appl. Phys. Lett.*, 67:866–868, 1995.

[176] G. Arlt and P. Sasko. Domain configuration and equilibrium size of domains in BaTiO$_3$ ceramics. *J. Appl. Phys.*, 51:4956–4960, 1980.

[177] D. Dimos, B. G. Potter, M. B. Sinclair, B. A. Tuttle, and W. L. Warren. Photo-induced and electrooptic properties of (Pb,La)(Zr,Ti)O$_3$ films for optical memories. *Integrated Ferroelectrics*, 5:47–58, 1994.

[178] M. Grossmann, O. Lohse, D. Bolten, T. Schneller, and R. Waser. The interface screening model as origin of imprint in PbZr$_x$Ti$_{1-x}$O$_3$ I dopant, illumination, and bias dependence. *J. Appl. Phys.*, 92:2680–1967, 2002.

[179] C. Elissalde and J. Ravez. Ferroelectric ceramics: Defects and dielectric relaxations. *J. Mater. Chem.*, 11:1957–1967, 2001.

[180] F. D. Morrison, D. C. Sinclair, and A. R. West. Characterization of lanthanum-doped barium titanate ceramics using impedance spectroscopy. *J. Am. Ceram. Soc.*, 84:531–538, 2001.

[181] T-C. Chen, C-T. Thio, and S-B. Desu. Impedance spectroscopy of SrBi$_2$Ta$_2$O$_9$ and SrBi$_2$Nb$_2$O$_9$. *J. Mater. Res.*, 12:2628–2637, 1997.

[182] S. S. N. Bharadwaja and S. B. Krupanidhi. Growth and study of antiferroelectric lead zirconate thin films by pulsed laser ablation. *J. Appl. Phys.*, 86:5862–5869, 1999.

[183] T. Kala. Electronic properties of Pb(Zr,Ti)O$_3$ solid solutions. *Phase Transitions*, 36:65–88, 1991.

[184] Y. Zhang and I. Baturin. *unpublished*.

[185] C.P. Lindsey and G.D. Patterson. Detailed comparison of the Williams-Watts and Cole-Davidson functions. *J. Chem. Phys.*, 73:3348–3357, 1980.

[186] Y. Ishibashi. Polarization reversals in ferroelectrics. In *Ferroelectric Thin Films: Synthesis and Basic Properties, C. Paz de Araujo, J.F. Scott, G.W. Taylor, Eds., Ferroelectricity and Related Phenomena, Vol. 10, Gordon and Breach, Amsterdam*, pages 135–151, 1996.

[187] H. Orihara, S. Hasimoto, and Y. Ishibashi. A theory of D-E loop based on the Avrami Model. *J. Phys. Soc. Jap.*, 63:1031–1035, 1994.

[188] R. V. Chamberlain. Experiments and theory of the non exponential relaxation in liquids, glasses, polymers and crystals. *Phase Transitions*, 65:169, 1998.

[189] D. Viehland and Y. H. Chen. Random-field model for ferroelectric domain dynamics and polarization reversal. *J. Appl. Phys.*, 88:6696–6707, 2000.

[190] O. Lohse, M. Grossmann, U. Boettger, D. Bolten, and R. Waser. Relaxation mechanism of ferroelectric switching in Pb(Zr,Ti)O$_3$ thin films. *J. Appl. Phys.*, 89:2332–2336, 2001.

[191] W. Kleemann. Random-field induced antiferromagnetic, ferroelectric and structural domain states. *Int. J. Mod. Phys.*, 7:2469–2507, 1993.

[192] W. Kleemann. Correlated domain dynamics in relaxor ferroelectrics and random-field systems. *Phase Transitions*, 65:141–157, 1998.

[193] Y. Imry and S.-K. Ma. Random-field instability of the ordered state of continuous symmetry. *Phys. Rev. Lett.*, 35:1399–1401, 1975.

[194] W. Kleemann, J. Dec, P. Lehnen, R. Blinc, B. Zalar, and R. Pankrath. Uniaxial relaxor ferroelectrics: The ferroic random-field Ising model materialized at last. *Europhys. Lett.*, 57:14–19, 2002.

[195] V. Ya. Shur, E. L. Rumyantsev, and S. Makarov. Kinetics of phase transformations in real finite systems: Application to switching in ferroelectrics. *J. Appl. Phys.*, 84:445–451, 1998.

[196] G. Arlt and J. H. Calderwood. Coercive and switching fields in ferroelectric ceramics. *Appl. Phys. Lett.*, 81:2605, 2002.

[197] R. G. Palmer, D. L. Stein, E. Abrahams, and P. W. Anderson. Models of hierarchically constrained dynamics for glassy relaxation. *Phys. Rev. Lett.*, 53:958–961, 1984.

[198] D. Hoffmann. Diploma Thesis. *Material Science, Darmstadt University of Technology*, 1999.

[199] G. Arlt. A model for switching and hysteresis in ferroelectric ceramics. *Integrated Ferroelectrics*, 16:229–236, 1997.

[200] J. C. Philips. Microscopic theory of the Kohlrausch relaxation constant β_k. *J. Non-Cryst. Solids*, 98:172–174, 1994.

[201] A. Diaz-Sanchez, A. Perez-Garrido, A. Urbina, and J.D. Catala. Stretched exponential relaxation for growing interfaces in quenched disordered media. *Phys. Rev. E*, page 031403, 2002.

[202] P. Nagels. Experimental Hall effect data for a small-polaron semiconductor. In C. L. Chien and C. R. Westgate, editors, *The Hall Effect and Its Applications*, pages 253–280. Plenum Press, NY and London, 1979.

[203] M. Dawber. Charge Transport Properties of Ferroelectric Thin Film Memories. *PhD Thesis: University of Cambridge, England*, 2003.

Curriculum Vitae

Education

Lycée A. Brugière, Clermont-Ferrand (France)	(9/89 - 6/92)
Lycée B. Pascal, Clermont-Ferrand	
Classes Préparatoires aux grandes Ecoles	(9/92 - 6/95)
Ecole Supérieure de L'Energie et des Matériaux	
Orléans (France)	
M. S. Materials Science	(9/95 - 6/97)
Darmstadt University of Technology	
M. S. Materials Science	(10/97 - 2/00)
Ph. D. Materials Science	(1/01 - 12/03)

Experience

Darmstadt University of Technology, Ph. D. Research	(01/01 - 12/03)
University of Cambridge, Visiting Researcher	(10/02 - 12/02)
Darmstadt University of Technology, Undergraduate Research Assistant	(5/96 - 3/98)
Heraeus GmbH, Research and Development	(6/97 - 8/97)
Manufacture Francaise des Pneumatiques Michelin, Practical Training	(7/96 - 8/96)

Military Service

Deutsche Französische Brigade, Müllheim	(03/00 - 12/00)

Refereed Publications

C. Verdier, D. C. Lupascu, J. Rödel, "Unipolar fatigue of ferroelectric lead zirconate titanate", *J. Europ. Ceram. Soc.*, 23, pp. 1409-1415, 2003

C. Verdier, D. C. Lupascu, J. Rödel, "Stability of defects after unipolar fatigue of lead-zirconate-titanate", *Appl. Phys. Let.*, 81, pp. 2596-2599, 2002

C. Verdier, D. C. Lupascu, "Fatigue anisotropy in lead zirconate titanate, ", *J. Europ. Ceram. Soc.*, accepted 2004

D. C. Lupascu, S. Fesodov, C. Verdier, J. Rödel, H. von Seggern, "Stretched exponential relaxation in perovskite ferroelectrics after cyclic loading", *J. Appl. Phys.*, 95, pp. 1386-1390, 2004

C. Verdier, D. C. Lupascu, H. von Seggern, J. Rödel, "Effect of thermal annealing on switching dynamics of fatigued lead zirconate titanate", *to be published*, 2004

C. Verdier, F. D. Morrison, M. Dawber, J. F. Scott, "Impedance spectroscopy-fatigue correlated investigations in bulk lead-zirconate-titanate", *to be published*, 2004

Oral Presentations

C. Verdier, F.D. Morrison, D.C. Lupascu, M. Dawber, J. Rödel, J.F. Scott "Microstructural characterization of fatigued lead zirconate titanate using impedance spectroscopy", 10th European Meeting of Ferroelectricity, Cambridge, England, 2003

Posters

C. Verdier, D. C. Lupascu, J. Rödel, "Unipolar versus bipolar fatigue in PZT", Electroceramics 2002, Rom, Italy, 2002

C. Verdier, D. C. Lupascu, J. Rödel, "Fatigue in bulk PZT", 10th International Meeting of Ferroelectricity, Madrid, Spain, 2001